# HISTORY OF PARTICLE THEORY

## Between Darwin and Shakespeare

**Other Related Titles from World Scientific**

---

*A Day at CERN: Guided Tour Through the Heart of Particle Physics*
by Gautier Depambour
ISBN: 978-981-122-110-1
ISBN: 978-981-122-064-7 (pbk)

*Loop Quantum Gravity for Everyone*
by Rodolfo Gambini and Jorge Pullin
ISBN: 978-981-121-195-9

*Did Time Begin? Will Time End?: Maybe the Big Bang Never Occurred*
by Paul H Frampton
ISBN: 978-981-4280-58-7

*The Encyclopedia of Cosmology*
*(In 4 Volumes)*
*Volume 1: Galaxy Formation and Evolution*
*Volume 2: Numerical Simulations in Cosmology*
*Volume 3: Dark Energy*
*Volume 4: Dark Matter*
Editor-in-chief: Giovanni G Fazio
by Rennan Barkana, Shinji Tsujikawa and Jihn E Kim
edited by Kentaro Nagamine
ISBN: 978-981-4656-19-1 (Set)
ISBN: 978-981-4656-22-1 (Vol. 1)
ISBN: 978-981-4656-23-8 (Vol. 2)
ISBN: 978-981-4656-24-5 (Vol. 3)
ISBN: 978-981-4656-25-2 (Vol. 4)

# HISTORY OF PARTICLE THEORY

## Between Darwin and Shakespeare

**Paul H Frampton**
**Jihn E Kim**

NEW JERSEY • LONDON • SINGAPORE • BEIJING • SHANGHAI • HONG KONG • TAIPEI • CHENNAI • TOKYO

*Published by*

World Scientific Publishing Co. Pte. Ltd.
5 Toh Tuck Link, Singapore 596224
*USA office:* 27 Warren Street, Suite 401-402, Hackensack, NJ 07601
*UK office:* 57 Shelton Street, Covent Garden, London WC2H 9HE

**Library of Congress Cataloging-in-Publication Data**
Names: Frampton, Paul H., author. | Kim, Jihn E., author.
Title: History of particle theory : between Darwin and Shakespeare /
Paul H. Frampton, Jihn E. Kim.
Description: Hackensack : World Scientific Publishing Co. Pte. Ltd., 2020. | Includes index.
Identifiers: LCCN 2020029270 | ISBN 9789811224652 (hardcover) |
ISBN 9789811224669 (ebook) | ISBN 9789811224676 (ebook other)
Subjects: LCSH: Particles (Nuclear physics)--History.
Classification: LCC QC793.16 .F73 2020 | DDC 539.7/201--dc23
LC record available at https://lccn.loc.gov/2020029270

**British Library Cataloguing-in-Publication Data**
A catalogue record for this book is available from the British Library.



For any available supplementary material, please visit
https://www.worldscientific.com/worldscibooks/10.1142/11948#t=suppl

Desk Editor: Ng Kah Fee

Typeset by Stallion Press
Email: enquiries@stallionpress.com

# Contents

# Preface

This is a popular book about the history of particle theory, the study of the smallest particles of matter.

We must explain the peculiar choice of subtitle, *Between Darwin and Shakespeare*, which might at first appear to have no connection to physics. In part, we wanted a catchy subtitle that has never been used before.

The first of our two subtitular heroes Charles Darwin (1809–1882) achieved immortality by his publication of *The Origin of Species* in 1859. It transformed the subject of theoretical biology by introducing and making convincing arguments for natural selection and evolution. In our popular book, we wish to describe the evolution of the physics of particle theory up to the 21st century, quite analogous to Darwin's discussions of evolution in biology, because there is a similar natural selection between theories based on those which agree with experiment; it is likewise a survival of the fittest.

Darwin was born in England in the west midland town of Shrewsbury in Shropshire, only 35 miles from the birthplace of the first-named author of this book in Kidderminster. Darwin had a middle-class upbringing and even in childhood showed interest in collecting and classifying beetles. In fact, he eventually displayed his talents in collecting and classifying anything biological, whether it be insects, birds, animals, fish, or plants. He had exceptional ability to think deeply for very long periods of time, sometimes years, about the specific topic he was studying.

Although we shall discuss only in the tenth and final chapter of our book our second subtitled man, William Shakespeare (1564–1616), it is worth mentioning here that Shakespeare was born in Stratford-upon-Avon, which is also 35 miles from Kidderminster in the opposite direction from Shrewsbury. Thus, Frampton was born midway between Darwin and Shakespeare, which led to our book's subtitle, which both of us immediately liked, at a September 2019 conference within the grounds of Mon Repos Palace, where the Duke of Edinburgh was born, in Corfu, Greece. Kim was born in Gurye, South Korea, about as far from England as it is possible to be while staying within Eurasia. Our subtitle does not imply that one author contributed more than the other.

To introduce our book, we begin (Chapter 1) 3,000 years ago with the ancient Greeks, notably Democritus who introduced atoms and Archimedes who was one of the leading Greek mathematicians. From then until the renaissance, religion played a significant role (Chapter 2) in the development of scientific ideas all the way up to Galileo Galilei's confrontation with the Catholic church.

The renaissance (Chapter 3) is characterised by a series of scientific giants who broke away from many of the Greek traditions and evolved the scientific method where theory must be confronted with experimental and observational data. A singular role was played by Isaac Newton (Chapter 4) who systematically created the field of theoretical physics, especially with his masterpiece, the *Principia*, published in 1687. His law of universal gravitation changed everything by showing that mathematical laws successfully described not only terrestrial experiments but also the motions of the heavenly bodies.

In Chapter 5, we discuss the 19th-century progress made by Boltzmann who assumed the existence of atoms in his work on the second law of thermodynamics. We also discuss Maxwell and his classical theory of electricity and magnetism. In the first part of the 20th century came the quantum revolution, but by the mid-1930s the list of elementary particles included only the proton, neutron, electron, photon, and the suggested neutrino.

From here, the modern particle theory evolves more rapidly. After WWII, quantum electrodynamics (QED) was successfully completed

(Chapter 6) and led to unprecedented agreement with experiment. To go beyond QED, two crucial steps took place in the 1950s both involving C.N. Yang, the creation of the Yang–Mills theory, or gauge field theory, and the discovery of parity violation. At the same time, a proliferation of strongly interacting particles was discovered by experimentalists.

This chaotic situation (Chapter 7) was organised by M. Gell-Mann who discovered an SU(3) classification which successfully predicted the $\Omega^-$ particle and led to the idea of quarks. The unification of QED with weak interactions (Chapter 8) to an electroweak theory was initiated by Glashow, combined with the BEH mechanism by Weinberg and Salam, then completed by Glashow, Iliopoulos, and Maiani. Gauging colour in quantum chromodynamics (QCD) provided a successful theory for strong interactions and completed the standard model.

All of this remarkable progress leaves many unanswered questions (Chapter 9) including the many parameters in the standard model and the fact that only 5% of the energy of the universe is in the form of normal matter while the rest is in the yet unexplained forms of dark matter and dark energy.

We finish our book idiosyncratically with Chapter 10 which has no *a priori* connection with Chapters 1–9. We combine questions and comments about particle theory with quotations from Shakespeare, an Englishman with an intellect probably comparable to that of Darwin and Newton, this time in the field of English literature.

What are our qualifications? Between us, we have 100 years of experience in publishing papers about particle theory, so we have worked through the gauge theory revolution since its beginning and have this opportunity to step back and take a look from our personal perspective at the developments in the last 50 years, while in this history book, we shall begin from a time nearly 3,000 years ago.

Some other popular books on particle theory published recently include Frank Close: *The Infinity Puzzle*, Basic Books (2013); John Iliopoulos: *The Origin of Mass*, Oxford (2017); and Alvaro De Rujula: *Enjoy Our Universe*, Oxford (2018). We recommend all these books. Our book is different from, and complementary to, them and provides our own historical view of a truly fascinating field.

Our intended readers are educated non-scientists and scientists, and especially young people considering a career in scientific research in general and in particle theory in particular.

Paul H. Frampton and Jihn E. Kim<br>Luxor, Egypt<br>January 2020

# Acknowledgements

This project was casually started at Café Aktaion, looking at the old Castle of Corfu, during the recepton meeting of the *Workshop on Connecting Insights in Fundamental Physics: Standard Model and Beyond*, held in Corfu Island in the summer of 2019. So, we are greatly indebted to the organizer of this workshop, George Zoupanos, on the current atomic theory. He mentioned in the opening speech of the conference the stories of the ancient Greek philosophers, and even touched on the earlier story on Odyssey after the Trojan War, having lived here in Kanoni, Corfu, for 10 years before returning to his wife.

The first author thanks all the colleagues and students who have added to his knowledge of particle theory over the past 50 years. At an educational level, Simon Altmann was his tutor at Brasenose College, Oxford, as an undergraduate, John Clayton Taylor was his DPhil supervisor in Oxford as a postgraduate, and Yoichiro Nambu was his first postdoc mentor in Chicago. From all of these people he learned an enormous amount about physics. It was a unique opportunity to collaborate with Sheldon Glashow for over two decades during which they wrote 13 papers. Selected physicists who have taught him a lot include Gerard 't Hooft, Lars Brink, Peter Goddard, Cecilia Jarlskog, Tom Kephart, Peter Minkowski, and Holger Nielsen. Apologies to the very many other physicists not explicitly mentioned but who nevertheless provided collegiality.

The second author deeply thanks Chong-Hyun Park who is an Academician on Greek Philosophy in Korea National Academy of

Science. Dr. Park translated all of Plato's Greek dialogues and provide a vivid view on the old Greek society. The narration on the Greek period in this book was carefully commented by their Greek colleague Emmanuel Paschos, probably the best physicist aware of the ancient stories of Greeks and the Dark Ages. On Catholitism, their friend Stephen Barr, the author of *Modern Physics and Ancient Faith*, carefully commented on the initial narration on the Dark Ages. The second author also thanks the chief priest of a Korean Buddhist temple Yakcheon-Sa, Dr. Sung Ku Kim, for laboriously explaining the story of Buddha's teaching. The authors also thank MooYoung Choi, A. Karpov, Young Duk Kim, Seo-Dong Shin, Kietae Rhie, Yannis Rizos, Jose Valle, and John Vergados for valuable suggestions. JEK's deepest debt of gratitute is to Hyo Hee for safe advice and to Saem for drawing beautiful figures.

# Prologue

Tens of thousand years ago, fears felt in dark nights led our ancestors to develop various religions. Still, in the modern scientific society, God from this origin is the revered one and the phrase God's design is used in the most advanced atomic theory. Atomic theory and God clash, which we narrate with the sentiment of Shakespearean phrases.

The size of a religion depends on the communal size having a mutually shared visible thing. Villagers with an impressive tree believed that tree to be a god. People of several villages around a memorable mountain believed that mountain to be a mountain god. A big society with a common historical background believed in the same things.

In Korea, there used to be a Sunghwangdang (or Seo-nang Dang) at the mouth of the village or the ridge of the head, and there is a tree, or trees, that is usually believed to be a guardian god. It is a pile of stones piled up in a conical shape. The people who came to this place passed by with stones, trees, and five-coloured cloths. The villagers believed that the god Seo-nang would protect their village.

Around the Mediterranean, ancient people believed in multiple gods, as noticed from the Egyptian, Greek, and Roman gods. These multiple gods are the remnants of their environment and/or their previous history. The Mediternanean is sometimes rough and sometimes calm, which is believed to be the act of Poseidon. Wine is favoured there and they needed the wine god Dyonisus. Volcanos, in Sinai and Vesevius, lightening, and thunder are believed to be the acts of Jupiter.

According to Singmund Freud's book *Totem and Taboo*, many gods in the ancient Egypt are the evolution from the time of apes.[1] A group of monkeys or apes had an alpha male whose gene is transmitted to its offsprings. The juvenile male kids dreamed of being an alpha male in a group in the future. Reaching adolescence and becoming strong, the son ape kills its father and takes the seat of an alpha male. Early humans had this earlier memory and felt sorry for their fathers, and had an annual ceremony to worship their fathers, sacrificing an animal, mostly a sacred sheep, which is kept clean for a year. In fact, this carnivalism ceremony had been transmitted to Moses' era and still remaines as communion in the Catholic Church. Animal gods in the ancient Egyptian polytheism must have arisen from this early human history with more animals added for their roles.

One god Aten was introduced by Paraoh Akhenaten (1354 BC–1336 BC) in the 18th Kingdom of Egypt. His original name was Amenhotep IV and he changed his name after introducing Aten. The bust of Akhenaten's wife Nefertiti is displayed in the Egyptian Museum in Berlin.

Moses' Jehovah is the unique God in the universe, presumably affected by Akhenaten's Aten. But, it differs from Aten in His most important role. Jehovah created the universe in 6 days as depicted in the first chapter of Genesis. The Christian idea of creation is eloquently depicted by Michelangelo in the Sistine Chapel at Vatican, Fig. 1. Creation of the universe is a very strong argument for the god Jehovah. A Christian asks the following, looking at a table:

Christian: Who made this table?
Spectator: A carpenter.
Christian: Can the table exist without the carpenter?
Spectator: No.
Christian: Who made you?
Spectator: I don't know.
Christian: As the table, you are made by a creator.

This is one theme of this book: God's design of the universe.

---

[1]S. Freud, *Totem and Taboo*, reprint edition (Dover Publications, 2018).

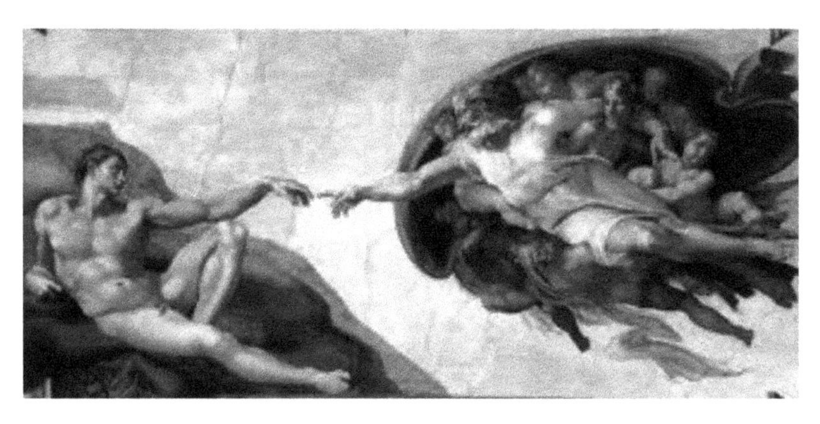

Figure 1: Michelangelo's Adam created by God at the Sistine Chapel, Vatican.

The beginning of the universe is a mystery in a few religions and in the atomic theory. Here, the difference is that religion is in the realm of belief and the modern atomic theory is constructed on evidence. Not all scientific disciplines and religions question the beginning. There is one such scientific theory under the name of static state of the universe. An oriental religion Buddhism does not admit the creation of the universe. Islam and Christianity, after passing through the Dark Ages, talk about the afterlife, but the Greek and Roman gods did not talk if it. Religion is based on beliefs and a requirement that its followers observe the most effective way to fulfil their beliefs.

In the ancient Greek and Roman times, *natural philosophy* was studied to look for the way in which Nature works. Our atomic theory has roots in the *natural philosophy* of the classical Greek period and possibly Buddhism since there were East–West exchanges, most notably at the time of Alexander. The Buddhism philosophy sounds similar to the Greek atomic theory, but it is not the same on the issue of creation of the universe.

As a natural philosophy but not as a religion, we cite God's design as one dogma for scientific theories. There is a very different dogma for creation. It is the natural selection theory of Charles Darwin and Alfred Russel Wallace.

In our field, in the physical sciences, the evolution theory is strongly believed by scientifically dating the extinction time of

Figure 2: An evolution cartoon.

dinosaurs based on the event of the big meteorite collision 65 million years ago. It was originally proposed in 1980 by a team of scientists led by Luis Alvarez and his son Walter Alvarez. Geologist Walter Alvarez was doing geological research at Gubbio in central Italy. There, he had located an outcrop on the walls of a gorge whose limestone layers included strata both above and below the Cretaceous–Paleogene boundary. Exactly at the boundary was a thin layer of clay, which turned out to contain more Iridium than normal. Thus, he with the help of his father, nuclear physicist Luis Alvarez, he hypothesised that the layer is from the dust of a meteorite. A crater was found in the Gulf of Mexico's Yucatan Peninsula. The extinction of dinosaurs was the beginning of the booming mammal era, finally resulting in humans.

Particle physics, a grandson of atomic theory aims at finding the ultimate laws of the universe. But, after decades of research, a satisfactory route has not yet been found. As such, many famous and leading physicists resort to the anthropic principle, the view that out of almost infinite possibilities in the beginning of the universe, we live in the one that fits to the evolution to us here and now. It belongs to the evolution dogma. A cartoon of human evolution from apes to the current atomists, even questioning the very beginning of the universe, is shown in Fig. 2.

In the Dark Ages, i.e. before the Renaissance, Plato and Aristotle were embraced by Christianity and Epicurus was abandoned. Christianity has its origin in Moses who adopted the monotheism from Pharaoh Akhenaton in the 18th Kingdom (13–14 BCE) of Egypt. We attribute the deterministic principle to this monotheism, and to Shakespeare because his plays have a deterministic plot from the first line.

# Chapter 1

# Ancient Greeks

The beginning of *The Feynman Lectures on Physics* states the following:

> "If, in some cataclysm, all of scientific knowledge were to be destroyed, and only one sentence passed on to the next generations of creatures, what statement would contain the most information in the fewest words? I believe it is the atomic hypothesis. In that one sentence, you will see, there is an enormous amount of information about the world, if just a little imagination and thinking are applied."

The great American physicist Richard Feynman considered atomic theory to be the most important scientific achievement of human intelligence (see Fig. 1).

Modern physical science is an offspring of atomic theory, as noticed from Mendeleev's periodic table from 150 years ago in 1869, culminating in current particle physics. We will discuss the current status of particle theory which has its roots in the natural philosophy of the classical Greek period. Roughly the first half of this book is devoted to the stories from the Greek period to WWII, and the second half to the establishment of the current particle theory in the last 70 years.

Let us start with Democritus, who is an important character in the theme of the book. Then, an opposite view is presented, that taken by Plato. These two are the ancient Greek counterparts to the two mentioned in our book title. However, they were influenced by philosophers who investigated the same topic, following the principle

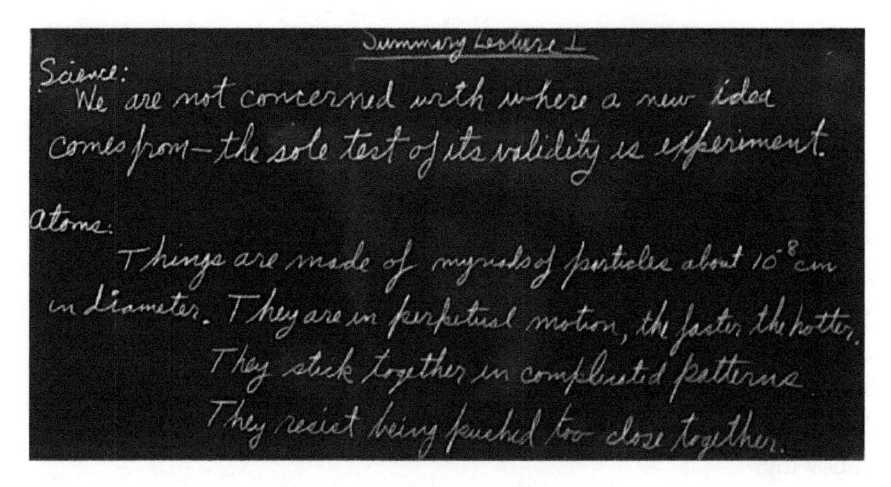


Figure 1: Feynman's blackboard.

that there is a rational explanation to the physical world. Thus, various schools related to the topic (in Ionia, in Athens, in Magna Graecia, and in Alexandria) will be briefly mentioned (see Fig. 2).

The origin of atomism is credited to a remarkable Greek natural philosopher Democritus (460 BC–370 BC) of Abdera, Thrace. He was born in the 80th Olympiad (460 BC–457 BC) according to Apollodorus of Athens. He lived in the first classical period of the Greek tradition. Greek philosophy is said to have begun in 585 BC when Thales of Miletus predicted the eclipse of the Sun and ended when the Academy of Athens closed in 529 AD as a result of the East Roman Emperor Justinian's stopping of its financial support. The period 2,500 years ago when Democritus worked was when the first problems were encountered. The first philosophers had the problem of defining the concepts, and Greek is accurate on this account compared to Latin and English. Science today has its jargon. For example, we use "flavour" and "colour" for properties of elementary particles, but we adopt these just for naming.

The first philosophers' definition turns out to be consistent with later use. The noun *kosmos* derives from a verb meaning "to order", "to arrange", and "to marshal". Thus, what the first Greek philosophers meant by *kosmos* was an orderly arrangement. Our use of the cosmos is the universe, the totality of things, but it

Figure 2: A map of ancient Greek city states. Magna Graecia was the coastal areas of southern Italy, and Ionia included islands Chios and Samos and nearby four city states.

is an ordered universe. The word *physics* derives from a verb "to grow". Growing things, plants, animals, and moving planets, are different from stones at rest. Thus, *physics* meant study of nature in contrast to artificial items, and corresponds to the present-day science. A cause is needed for movement. The word *arche* cognates from a verb meaning "to begin", "to commence", "to rule", and "to govern". Writers on early Greek philosophy use *arche* to mean principle, which is not different from our current understanding. It is said that *arche* was first used by Anaximander. Nature is the principle and origin of growth.

Gautama Buddha (624 BC–544 BC) was an enlightened teacher. The correct date of Buddha's death was in dispute before 1956 AD, but it was declared officially in the sixth official meeting of Buddhist monks that that year was the 2,500 year anniversary of Buddha's death. According to Buddha's teaching, all beings come into being or cease to be, based on the causes and conditions which brought them into existence. In other words, they arise or cease only through interdependent relationships. The chief priest of the Buddhist temple Yakcheonsa, Sung Ku Kim (once an active quantum field theorist), says that the law of relationships or the theory of links — *yeonkibeob* in Korean — is the first principle of Buddhist philosophy. Without using the word creation, nothing exists on its own independent of anything else. Buddha's teaching starts with *brahman* (meaning all in the universe in Sanskrit) and *atman* (real thing possessing the *brahman*). Around the same time when the first Greek philosophers (for example, Thales (624–623 BC to 548–545 BC)) anguished over defining the words including *kosmos*, Buddha taught his enlightenment to students in terms of *brahman* and *atman*, the self that possesses the faculties of feeling, understanding, will, and consciousness. Unlike the four elements of Plato, Buddhism does not allow creation of *atman* out of *brahman*. There are links only between *atman*.

The original writings on papyrus books of two and half millennia ago have not survived the time, largely due to the effects of climate and pests. The oldest writing on papyrus is the 4,500-year-old logbook Diary of Merer, recording transportation of casting stones to Giza from Tura, for Khufu's Pyramid. It was found in a cave in Wadi al-Jarf on the dry Red Sea coast by archeologist Pierre Tallet in 2013. But, most books have not survived. Even if books from classical antiquity survived the perils of fire, raindrops from the library ceiling, or wear from excessive readings, they could not escape white-silver shiny bookworms. Aristotle presumed the existence of tiny bookworms, which were finally seen by Robert Hooke through a microscope in 1655. These worms are called "teeth of time" in *The Swerve* by Stephen Greenblatt. Writings in classical antiquity were on papyrus papers which are made from the 40-cm papyrus stems soaked in the Nile. The insect "teeth of time" finds this papyrus and nibbles away books like wood-eating ants destroying wooden structures over time. So, it was important that the writings of the first philosophers be copied for the next generations. When copied by scribes, there must have been errors or intended changes.

Between classical antiquity and now, the prodigious writer Simplicius of Sicily (c. 490–560) commented extensively on the works of Aristotle and others from which most of our information on the first philosophers is derived. Simplicius must have used copies of copies of copies of Lucretius' copy of copies of Aristotle. The thoughts of the first philosophers were commented on by Aristotle and others in what are called "fragments" from which we understand the works of the first philosophers. Atomism of the classical antiquity arrives to us through Aristotle's fragments, Simplicius' translation, repeatedly copied by scribes in Christian monasteries in the Dark Ages dominated by Christianity, and Poggio's discovery of Lucretius' poems[1]:

> "Fear holds dominion over mortality
> Only because seeing in land and sky
> So much the course whereof no wise they knew,
> . . . . . . . . . . . .
> But each might grow from any stock or limb
> By chance and change, Indeed, and were there not
> For each its procreant atoms, could things have
> . . . . . . . . . . . .
> But yet creation's neither crammed nor blocked
> About by body: there's in things a void–
> . . . . . . . . . . . .
> Thus primal bodies are solid, without void."

What Lucretius wrote is that the material of the universe is an infinite number of atoms moving randomly in the void (space). Now, most sources credit Democritus as the first atomist. His exact contributions are difficult to disentangle from those of his mentor Leucippus, as they are often mentioned together in texts. None of his writings have survived; only fragments are known from his vast body of work. Leucippus, the founder of atomism, was the greatest influence upon him. He and Democritus praise Anaxagoras. Most sources say that Democritus followed in the tradition of Leucippus

[1]T. L. Carus, *On The Nature of Things* (in English) (Enhanced EBooks Publishing, USA, 2015), Book I.

and that they carried on the scientific rationalist philosophy associated with the school in Miletus. Both were thoroughly materialist, believing everything to be the result of natural laws. Unlike Aristotle or Plato, the atomists attempted to explain the world without reasoning as to purpose, prime mover,[2] or final cause. The atomists' questions of physics should be answered with a purely mechanistic question, "What earlier circumstances caused this event?", while their opponents search for "explanations" (*logos*), in addition to the material and mechanistic (see Fig. 3).

The atomistic void hypothesis was a response to the paradoxes of Parmenides and Zeno in Elea, the founders of metaphysical logic, who put forth arguments difficult to answer. To draw no movement in Democritus' atomic theory, Parmenides and Zeno held that any movement would require a void — which is nothing — but a nothing cannot exist. The position of Eleatic school was "You say there is a void; therefore the void is not nothing; therefore there is not the void."

The atomists agreed that motion required a void, but simply ignored the argument of the Eleatic school on the grounds that motion was an observable fact. Therefore, they asserted, there must be a void. This idea survived in a refined version as Newton's theory of absolute space, which met the logical requirements of attributing reality to not being. Einstein's theory of relativity provided a new

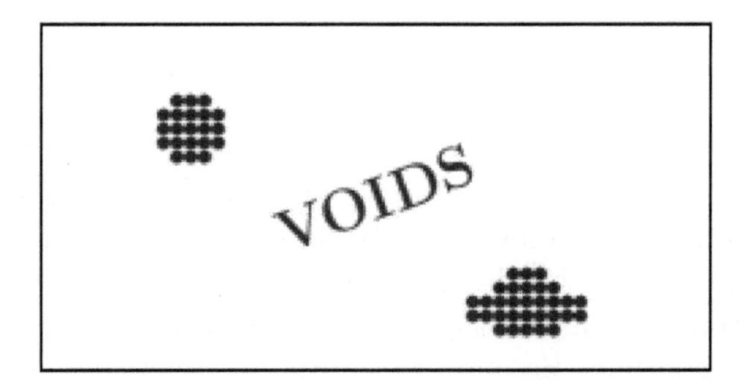


Figure 3: Democritus' view with individual atoms.

[2]Aristotle did not define the prime mover exactly and considered it as a general concept for the force that set the planets and universe in motion.

answer to Parmenides and Zeno, with the insight that space by itself is relative and cannot be separated from time as part of a generally curved space–time manifold. Consequently, Newton's refinement is now considered superfluous.

Also, there was the Athenian school started by Socrates (470 BC–399 BC) and succeeded by Plato (430 BC to 348–347 BC) and Aristotle (384 BC–322 BC). Socrates' philosophy is largely known by Plato's dialogues. Plato established a school of thought where he taught students and held seminars. He also founded the Academy, the first institution of higher learning in the Western world. Based on ancient sources, most modern scholars believe that he was born in Athens or Aegina between 429 BC and 423 BC, not long after the start of the Peloponnesian War. According to Neanthes of Cyzicus, Plato was 6 years younger than politician Isocrates who was born in 436 BC. He is widely considered the pivotal figure in the history of Ancient Greek and Western philosophy, along with his teacher, Socrates, and his most famous student, Aristotle. Plato has also often been cited as one of the founders of Western religion and spirituality. The so-called Neoplatonism of philosophers like Plotinus and Porphyry influenced Saint Augustine and thus Christianity. Alfred North Whitehead once noted, "the safest general characterisation of the European philosophical tradition is that it consists of a series of footnotes to Plato." Plato disliked Democritus, the founder of a competing philosophy, so much that he wished all of the latter's books burned. Democritus was nevertheless well known to his fellow Northern-born philosopher Aristotle.

As a follower of Pythagorean teaching, Plato liked mathematical reasoning about Nature. So, he associated each of the four classical elements (fire, air, earth, and water) with a regular solid (tetrahedron, octahedron, cube, and icosahedron) due to their shapes, the so-called Platonic solids, and movements to golden ratios of numbers. He associated the fifth regular solid, the dodecahedron, to introducing time. Farmers in early civilisations needed to know the perfect time to plant their crops. Humans began to observe the Sun's passage through a fixed point and this practice distinguished seasons. The Sun's movement is time and hence the heavenly objects are related to time. These regular solids have fundamental faces, regular triangle, square, and regular pentagon. Even Werner Heisenberg mentioned[3] the beauty (or symmetry) of Plato's geometrical objects: "In Plato's Timaeus, finally fundamental particles are not shapeless but mathematical objects."

In Plato's dialogues, Socrates and his company of disputants had something to say on many subjects, including several aspects of metaphysics. These include religion and science, human nature, love, and sexuality. More than one dialogue contrasts perception and reality, nature and custom, and body and soul. In the Timaeus (participants of the dialogue are Timaeus, Socrates, Hermocrates, and Critias), we find that Plato's "the good (*agathon* in Greek)" becomes the principle in the creation of the universe. *'Kosmos'* in Greek means "good, beautiful order". Plato named the creator as *dẽmiourgos*, meaning craftsman-like carpenter. A carpenter exercises his best in making a table, and so does *dẽmiourgos*, realising *agathon* in the process of creating the universe. *Dẽmiourgos* in the dialogue Timaeus is the deified expression of Plato's good and intelligence. Thus, Plato's creation is both metaphysical and technical. The Timaeus was translated into Latin first by Marcus Tullius Cicero around 45 BC and later by Calcidius in the 4th century AD. Cicero's fragmentary translation was highly influential in late antiquity, especially on Latin-speaking Church fathers such as Saint Augustine who did not appear to have access to the original Greek dialogue. Here, we follow a Korean translation from the Greek original by Korean experts on Plato's dialogues.[4]

Timaeus narrates that *Dẽmiourgos* creates the universe based on his principle of the good and intelligence. Initially, the four elements (fire, air, earth, and water) were shapeless traces of them, mixed and in constant motion in the space (*chòra*). To relate to reality by observation, Plato reasoned that you cannot see anything

---

[3]W. Heisenberg, *Physics and Philosophy: The Revolution in Modern Science* (Penguin Books, New York, 1962), p. 71.

[4]C-h. Park and Y-k. Kim, *Plato's Timaeus* in Korean (Seo Gwang Publishing Company, Seoul, Korea, 2000).

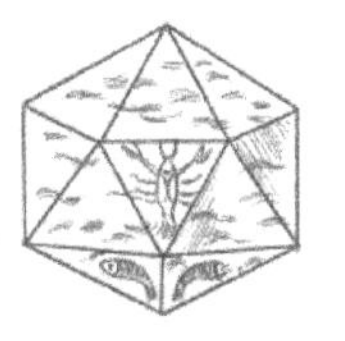
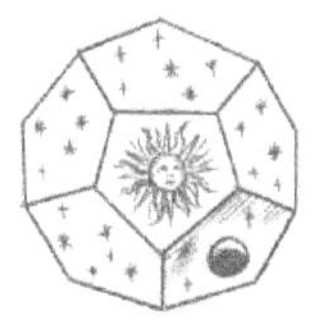

Figure 4: Plato's five regular solids and the corresponding elements.

without fire. Fire is the first element. Without earth, you cannot make solids. To have the continents, therefore, earth is the second element. To connect fire and earth, you need some flexible elements, which are air and water. Air and water are around the continent, and Fig. 4 places air and water around earth. In Fig. 4, the living creatures carrying the essence of these elements are inserted in the four regular solids. Then, *Dẽmiourgos* considered movements based on the patterns and the movement needed measuring time. For time, Plato related to the heavenly objects, Sun, Moon, planets, and stars. Out of these shapeless elements, *Dẽmiourgos* brought order and clarity, imitating (like a craftsman who follows a design) an unchanging and eternal model (*idea* or *paradeigma*). Timaeus travelled to Egypt and might have known Moses' story, but his "shapeless" and the one in the first sentence of Genesis, "When in the beginning God created the heavens and the earth, the earth being untamed and shapeless, God said, Let there be light!" are different according to Chong-Hyun Park. The meaning in the Genesis is creation out of nothing (*creatio ex nihilo* in Latin introduced by Christian philosophers and clergy) and Greeks' creation was "nothing is made out of nothing"(*ex nihilo nihilo fit* in Latin), namely, *Dẽmiourgos*' creation was making shapes with the substance, technically using *eidè* (polygons) and *arithmoi* (numbers). As a carpenter, *Dẽmiourgos* had a purpose and designed his imitation based on the most ideal. The heavenly objects are placed in the dodecahedron[5] with the Sun, the next important one beyond Earth, circling around it and others following the Sun or staying at one point, as shown in Fig. 5. The final shapes must be as beautiful

[5]Twelve is considered to be the number of heaven.

Figure 5: Plato's view of the universe in the dodecahedron.

(i.e., symmetric) as possible, ending up with five regular solids of Fig. 4.

- **God's design:** Plato's creation was a carpenter's work following a principle (*idea* or *paradeigma* in Greek). Moses' creation was out of nothing. In modern particle theory, the beauty and/or simplicity is frequently mentioned, which may be placed in Plato's principle. So, we put Shakespeare's ingenious design of the play in God's design.
- **Darwinism:** The universe evolves according to the natural laws but the ingredients (particles) are put in the hot soup with certain initial conditions. Here, one does not need God's hand of Fig. 1 in prologue. Even the initial conditions are better to be given by the natural laws. In this sense, basically Einstein's God means creation via Darwinism.

Plato's student Aristotle is considered to be the founder of the Peripatetic school of philosophy, opened in Lyceum in 335 BC, and Aristotelian tradition. Along with his teacher Plato, he has been called the 'Father of Western Philosophy'. According to Chong-Hyun Park, Aristotle was trying to escape from the aura of Plato. Aristotle's views on physical science written in *Peri Physeos* (*On Nature*) profoundly shaped medieval scholarship. Their influence extended from Late Antiquity and the Early Middle Ages into the Renaissance, and were not replaced systematically until the Enlightenment and theories such as classical mechanics. Aristotle considered one more element in addition to the four of Plato's: ether. The Greek word for ether is *pemtousia* which means the fifth substance.

Historians in the 19th century invented the word "Neoplatonism" which applied to the tradition of Plato. The first Neoplatonist was Plotinus (c. 204–205 AD to 270 AD) in Hellenistic Roman Egypt. His writings *Enneads* have inspired centuries of Pagan, Jewish, Christian, Gnostic, and Islamic metaphysicians and mystics.

The atomic theory was applied in everyday living by Epicurus (341 BC–270 BC), who was born 7 years after the death of Plato on the island Samos to Athenian parents. He turned against the Platonism of his day and established his own school, known as "the Garden', in Athens. His purpose of philosophy was to attain the happy, tranquil life, characterised by *ataraxia* (peace and freedom from fear) and *aponia* (the absence of pain) and by living a self-sufficient life surrounded by friends. He openly allowed women to join the school as a matter of policy. Epicurus and his followers were known for eating simple meals and discussing a wide range of philosophical subjects.

But, most knowledge of his teachings did not come from Greek originals but from the Latin written later by the Roman poet Titus Lucretius Carus or commonly Lucretius, the biographer Diogenes Laërtius, the statesman Cicero, and the philosophers Philodemus and Sextus Empiricus. He taught that death is the end of both the body and the soul and therefore should not be feared. Likewise, Epicurus taught that the gods, though they do exist, have no involvement in human affairs and do not punish or reward people for their actions. Nonetheless, he maintained that people should still behave ethically, not because of the 'goodness' mentioned by Plato but because of the burden of guilt which prevents them from attaining *ataraxia*.

Though popular, Epicurean teachings, *pursuit of happiness*, were controversial from the beginning in Athens which was the city of Plato. Epicureanism reached the height of its popularity during the late years of the Western Roman Republic, before declining as the rival school of Stoicism grew in popularity at its expense. It finally died out in late antiquity in the wake of early Christianity after Justinian's edict of 529 AD. Epicurus himself was popularly, though inaccurately, remembered throughout the Middle Ages as a patron of drunkards, whoremongers, and gluttons.

Of course, there were many philosophers in the first classical period who influenced the atomic theory and Plato's universe. The first person who thought deeply and deviated from the use of mythology to explain the world and the universe was Thales (624–623 BC to 548–545 BC) in the city state of Miletus in the ancient Greek Ionia. He is recognised as the first individual known to have entertained and engaged in scientific philosophy in Western civilisation, or more impressively the first since achieving cognitive faculty. He was one of the Seven Sages of Greece. The other Sages were politicians, Pittacus of Lesvos, Bias of Priene, Solon of Athens, Cleobulus of Lindos, Periander of Corinth, and Chilon of Sparta (Some cite Myson of Chenae and philosopher Anacharsis of Scythia, instead of Cleobulus and Periander). Thales was also a politician but is known better as the founder of the Ionian School. He proclaimed that the originating principle of nature and the nature of matter was a single material substance: water. Anaximander (610 BC–546 BC) succeeded Thales and became the second master of the Ionian School. Arguably, Pythagoras was one among his pupils. As mentioned before, Anaximander defined the word *arche* and is considered to be an early proponent of science and tried to observe and explain different aspects of the universe, with a particular interest in its origins, claiming that nature is ruled by laws.

Another ancient Ionian Greek philosopher who influenced philosophers of later times was Pythagoras who was the eponymous founder of Pythagoreanism. His political and religious teachings were well known in Magna Graecia and influenced Plato, Aristotle, and through them Western philosophy. Pythagoras was credited with many mathematical and scientific discoveries, including the Pythagoras theorem, Pythagorean tuning, and the five regular solids, which were admired by Plato. It was said that he was the first man to call himself a philosopher ('lover of wisdom'). Pythagorean ideas on mathematical perfection also impacted ancient Greek art. Pythagoras continued to be regarded as a great philosopher throughout the Middle Ages and his philosophy had a major impact on scientists such as Nicolaus Copernicus, Johannes Kepler, and Isaac Newton.

Diogenes Laërtius (3rd century AD) states that Pythagoras "did not indulge in the pleasures of love" and that he cautioned others to only have sex "whenever you are willing to be weaker than yourself".

Parmenides and Zeno were born in Elea (560 BC–510 BC). Parmenides has been considered the founder of metaphysics or ontology and has influenced the whole history of Western philosophy. He was the founder of the Eleatic school of philosophy, which also included Zeno and Melissus of Samos. Zeno's paradox was perhaps the first example of a method of proof called *reductio ad absurdum*, literally meaning to reduce to the absurd. Zeno's paradoxes of motion were to defend Parmenides' view. The single known work by Parmenides is a poem, *On Nature*, only fragments of which survive, containing the first sustained argument in the history of philosophy. In it, Parmenides prescribes two views of reality. In "the way of truth" (a part of the poem), he explains how all reality is one, change is impossible, and existence is timeless, uniform, and necessary. In *the way of opinion*, Parmenides explains the world of appearances, in which one's sensory faculties lead to conceptions which are false and deceitful, yet he does offer a cosmology. Parmenides' philosophy has been explained with the slogan "whatever is is, and what is not cannot be". He is also credited with the phrase *ex nihilo nihilo fit* (out of nothing, nothing comes), commenting on *Dẽmiourgos*' creation.

Before Democritus, Heraclitus (535 BC–475 BC) in Ephesus talked about the world in *On Nature* but he was uncertain where to place some words. So, he is nicknamed "The Obscure" or "The Riddler". In *Rhetoric*, Aristotle described his style, "It is difficult to punctuate Heraclitus' writings because it is unclear whether a word goes with what follows or with what precedes it. E.g. at the very beginning of his treatise, where he says: *Of this account which holds forever men prove uncomprehending,* it is unclear which 'forever' goes with." He was author of *On Nature* which was dedicated to the great temple of Artemis, one of the Seven Wonders of the Ancient World. In *Lives of the Philosophers*, Diogenes Laërtius wrote, "They say that Euripides gave [Sokrates] a copy of Heraclitus' book and asked him what he thought of it. He replied: 'What I understand is splendid; and I think that what I don't understand is so too — but it would take a Delian diver to get to the bottom of it."' Hippolytus presents a summary of Heraclitus' main ideas in *Refutation of All Heresies*, "Heraclitus says that the universe is divisible and indivisible, generated and ungenerated, mortal and immortal, Word and Eternity, Father and Son, God and Justice."

In *Commentary on the Physics*, Simplicius writes the following:

> "In the first book of the *Physics*, Anaxagoras says that uniform stuffs, infinite in quantity, separate off from a single mixture, all things being present in all and each being characterized by what predominates. He makes this clear in the first book of the *Physics* at the beginning of which he says: Together were all things, infinite in quantity and in smallness..."

Here, Anaxagoras (510 BC–428 BC), born in Clazomenae and brought up in Athens, described the world as a mixture of primary imperishable ingredients, where material variation was never caused by an absolute presence of a particular ingredient, but rather by its relative preponderance over the other ingredients; in his words, "each one is ... most manifestly those things of which there are the most in it". It is very similar to our understanding of chemical elements by Mendeleev's table. But, he differs from Democritus' atoms in introducing the concept of *Nous* (Cosmic Mind) as an ordering force, which moved and separated from the original mixture, which was homogeneous, or nearly so. He, being two generations before Democritus, might have influenced him. One generation before Democritus, Empedocles (490 BC–430 BC), a citizen of Akragas in Sicily, held the view that the four elements (fire, earth, breath, and rain written in Lucretius' poem *De Rerum Natura*[6]) were those

[6]S. Greenblatt, *The Swerve: How the Renaissance Began* (W.W. Norton & Company, New York, 2011).

unchangeable fundamental realities. Plato had four elements, exactly the same as Empedocles', changing breath to air and rain to water. Influenced by Pythagoras (died c. 495 BC) and the Pythagoreans, Empedocles challenged the practice of animal sacrifice and killing of animals for food. He developed a distinctive doctrine of reincarnation. Not only a scientific thinker and a forerunner to physicists, he was also a firm believer in Orphic mysteries. Aristotle mentions Empedocles among the Ionic philosophers, and he places him in very close relation to the atomist philosophers and to Anaxagoras.

Philosophers before Socrates (470 BC–399 BC), the first philosophers in the early antiquity, are customarily mentioned as pre-Socratic. Socrates was an Athenian philosopher credited as one of the founders of Western philosophy, and as being the first moral philosopher of the Western ethical tradition of thought. An enigmatic figure, he had no writings, and is known chiefly through the accounts of classical writers writing after his lifetime, particularly his students Plato and Xenophon. Plato's dialogues are among the most comprehensive accounts of Socrates to survive from antiquity, from which Socrates has become renowned for his contributions to the fields of ethics and epistemology. It is this Platonic Socrates who lends his name to the concepts of Socratic irony and the Socratic method, or elenchus. However, questions remain regarding the distinction between the real-life Socrates and Plato's portrayal of Socrates in his dialogues. Socrates exerted a strong influence on philosophers in later antiquity and in the modern era. Depictions of Socrates in art, literature, and popular culture have made him one of the most widely known figures in the Western philosophical tradition.

The statement "I know that I know nothing" is often attributed to Socrates, based on a statement in Plato's *Apology*. The conventional interpretation of this is that Socrates's wisdom was limited to an awareness of his own ignorance. Socrates believed the best way for people to live was to focus on the *pursuit of virtue* rather than the pursuit, for instance, of material wealth and happiness. He always invited others to try to concentrate more on friendships and a sense of true community, for Socrates felt this was the best way for people to grow together as a populace. His actions lived up to this standard: in the end, Socrates accepted his death sentence when his accusers thought he would simply leave Athens.

It is worthwhile to mention a few mathematicians after Plato who himself can be considered as one. In the Greek-speaking Alexandria, the capital of Ptolemy Kingdom,[7] Euclid (325 BC–270 BC) wrote an encyclopedic treatise on all fields of mathematics, having written the integral knowledge of accumulated wisdom in Greece before. Being the best known among many, he may be regarded as the Father of Geometry. His remarkable book *Elements* provided an axiomatic logically coherent framework to discuss geometry on a two-dimensional flat plane involving parallel lines, similar and isosceles triangles. Euclid had the longest lasting impact of any ancient Greek mathematician as his textbook remained in use until the 20th century over 2,200 years later. Little is known about his life or how much of *Elements* was based on his own versus others' discoveries.

It is remarkable that it was not until the 19th century that somebody discussed geometry on a curved surface such as on a sphere where parallel lines meet and that the angles of a triangle do not add to 180°, and so the Euclidean axioms fundamentally changed. This underlines just how simple and persuasive Euclid's presentations were.

There was a mathematician physicist Archimedes (287 BC–212 BC) in Syracuse, Sicily. He was one of the leading scientists of classical antiquity and generally regarded as the greatest mathematician among the ancient Greeks. He partially anticipated modern calculus by the concept of sum of infinitesimals. He made an accurate estimate of $\pi$ to two decimal places as $\pi \simeq 3.14$ and discovered that the area of a circle is given by $\pi R^2$, the volume of a sphere by $4\pi R^3/3$.

In order to determine whether the King's crown had been made of pure gold, he enunciated the principle that weight is reduced under water by the weight of water displaced. He is alleged to have run naked into the street shouting "Eureka" after making this discovery

[7]Even now there are more Greek speaking people in Alexandria than those in Greece.

while taking a bath, and went on to find that the crown-makers had indeed cheated the King.

Archimedes developed the idea of exponentiation to write large numbers. In mechanics, he contributed substantially to hydrostatics and to understanding the principles of levers. He invented a screw pump that is still used today. He designed a huge ship, *Syracusia*, the largest ship ever built at the time in which an Archimedean screw was used as the bilge pump.

Much more recently, Galileo described Archimedes' accomplishments as 'superhuman' and the Fields Medal, the most prestigious prize in mathematics, is emblazoned with his image.

Despite protective orders by superiors, Archimedes was killed erroneously by a Roman soldier at the age of 75.

In Alexandria, Egypt, there were Hero (10 AD–70 AD) and Ptolemy (100 AD–170 AD). Hero was an engineer and mathematician. He invented an *aelipile* (or Hero engine), which is the precursor of the steam engine which prompted the field of thermodynamics in the 19th century AD. Hero is responsible for Hero's formula in mathematics, which provides the area of a triangle from its side lengths. He also discovered methods for computing square roots and cube roots. Ptolemy was a mathematician, astronomer, and geographer. He wrote *Almagest*, the only surviving ancient treatise on astronomy. In it, he famously suggested a geocentric Ptolemaic Solar System, an idea which was generally accepted for 1,200 years until the work of Copernicus. He was certain that the Earth does not move, an idea firmly adopted by the Catholic church as Galileo found out to his peril. Ptolemy also contributed significantly to cartography, producing maps of Eurasia and Africa, which can be admired at the Royal Geographical Society in London. His maps are surprisingly good given their age, although not surprisingly they do contain entertaining mistakes when compared to any modern map.

To summarise Chapter 1, we started with the atomist Democritus and have described the accomplishments of over a dozen ancient Greeks, all with extraordinary intellects. The main achievements of antiquity were in philosophy including ethics, morals, and politics. These ideas remain a major influence in modern philosophy.

The overlap of science and modern ideas is necessarily less because the technology necessary to do useful experiments had not been developed since there were less data available. This is probably why the ancient Greeks depended more on philosophical speculations.

Nevertheless, modern physics has evolved in a Darwinian style from the atomism of Democritus and his school, who showed such remarkable prescience. Greeks admired Democritus, who was depicted on the 10-drachma coin before the switch to Euros. Of the ancient Greek mathematicans, Euclid and Archimedes founded the subject and set example for all later discoveries in mathematics.

Given all the intellectual progress between 600 BC and 100 BC, it can seem disappointing that only relatively small advances were made in the next 1,500 years.

## Chapter 2

# God's Plan

Immediately following the ancient Greeks, we should discuss Titus Lucretius Carus (99 BC–55 BC) who is considered to be the intellectual heir to Epicurus. He was a Greek Epicurean at the time of Julius Caesar (100 BC–44 BC) and the author of the remarkable, long poem *De Rerum Natura* (*On the Nature of Things*) written in Latin. Lucretius must have admired the atomism judging from his beautiful sentence, "the elements are like the letters of the alphabet where with 24 letters you can construct thousands of words." The original Latin *De Rerum Natura* written on papyrus consisted of 7,400 lines filling six books and must have been copied tens of times though papyrus survived impressively long. But, it was thought to have been lost to posterity until a copy from copies of copies of Simplicius of the 6th century AD was found in a German monastery in 1417 by Poggio Bracciolini (1380–1459).

A cultural hero Lucretius was a Prometheus in Greek mythology, and in the 20th century Robert Oppenheimer was called a modern Prometheus.[1] There must have been many admirers of Prometheus during the time of Caesar as the famous Roman statesman and orator Marcus Tullius Cicero (106 BC–43 BC) praised *De Rerum Natura* as "Poetry of Lucretius is rich in brilliant genius, yet highly artistic." The greatest Roman poet Virgil (70 BC–19 BC) was about 15 years old when Lucretius died and he must have read *De Rerum Natura*,

[1]K. Bird and M. J. Sherwin, *American Prometheus: The Triumph and Tragedy of J. Robert Oppenheimer* (Vintage Book Company, 2006).

judging from his youngster-style acclamation, "Blessed is he who has succeeded in finding out the cause of things".

The influence of the ancient Greeks at that time can be seen everywhere in Italy. The current name of Naples arises from Nea Polis (new city in Greek) due to Gordon Semenoff's interpretation, showing that Greek influenced so much in this region. From the remains in Pompei, archeologists find the influence of Greek philosophers in Rome. Lucretius belonged to the school of Epicurus, although Greenblatt's 2019 book *The Swerve*[2] cites that Philodemus (a Greek invited to Rome since Greek classicism was admired there) stayed in Rome at the time of Lucretius. So, the Epicurus school seems to be a Greek school at the time of Greek supremacy, specialising in Natural Laws.

The original Latin poem must have been admirable to Romans in the classical period even as the English translation with 7–9 words in a line muses beautifully:

> "Whilst human kind
> Throughout the lands lay miserably crushed
> Before all eyes beneath Religion–who
> Would show her head along the region skies
> Glowering on mortals with her hideous face–
> A Greek it was who first opposing dared
> Raise mortal eyes that terror to withstand,
> Whom nor the fame of Gods nor lightning's stroke
> Nor threatening thunder of the ominous sky
> Abashed; but rather chafed to angry zest
> His dauntless heart to be the first to rend
> The crossbars at the gates of Nature old."

It is not known to what extent actually Lucretius intended to convey the philosophy of Epicurus because this poem is through the 6th-century prodigeous pagan writer Simplicius. Still, Democritus was a generation earlier than Epicurus. This poem was given much publicity and importance in the book *The Swerve* by Steven

[2]S. Greenblatt, *The Swerve: How the Renaissance Began* (W.W. Norton & Company, New York, 2011).

Greenblatt published in 2011 and winner of a 2012 Pulitzer prize. Greenblatt suggested that the *De Rerum Natura* played a significant role in seeding the Renaissance. Whether true or not, the poem does contain in Lines 113–140 of Book II a truly remarkable atomistic description of Brownian motion, which was understood only two millennia later by Boltzmann (1872) and Einstein (1905), and which Lucretius regarded as proof of the existence of atoms.

Not surprisingly, his other scientific musings were less accurate. Although he suggested the idea that Nature experiments across aeons and that organisms have the best chance of survival when they best adapt in terms of strength, speed, and intellect, he did not anticipate what we now know as evolution. He did not recognise the superiority of humans to animals, which is a strong motive among God's plan of the universe.

Poggio's discovery of *De Rerum Natura* was made toward the end of Dark Ages or it may be better to say that it ended the Dark Ages. The reason that it was hidden so long was because Epicureanism was regarded as pagan by Christian leaders. For the book *De Rerum Natura* to be known to the masses, it must have been copied to a great extent. If purchase of *De Rerum Natura* were allowed, merchants must have copied it to get profit with whatever its cost. But, forbidden by Church elders, it was copied only in isolated monasteries in the Dark Ages. Copying it was not given preference in the isolated monasteries and there must have been some errors or puported corrections by scribes in the monasteries. In *The Swerve*, Stephen Greenblatt imagines a possible scene in a monastery scriptorium:

> "The monastery was a place of rules, but in the scriptorium there were rules within rules. Access was denied to all non-scribes. Absolute silence reigned. Scribes were not allowed to choose the particular books that they copied or to break the dead silence by requesting aloud from the librarian such books as they might wish to consult in order to complete the task that had been assigned them. An elaborate gestural language was invented in order to facilitate such requests as were permitted. If a scribe wanted to consult a psalter, he made the general sign for a book–extending

> his hands turning over imaginary pages–and then, by putting his hand on his hand in the shape of a crown, the specific sign for the Psalm of King David. If he was asking for a pagan book, he began, after making the general sign, to scratch behind his ear, like a dog scratching his fleas. And if he wished to have what the Church regarded as a particularly offensive or dangerous pagan book, he could put two fingers into his mouth, as if he were gagging."

In the middle of the Dark Ages, it must have not been possible for scribes to copy *De Rerum Natura* with ease, as only a few remaining ones today testify. In the early Roman Empire, alternatively called the late classical period, "paganism" was used for practicing polytheism, with gods of Jupiter, Neptune, Venus, etc. The early Christians in the 4th century practiced polytheism because it was practiced in rural and provincial areas compared to the Christian population in the big cities. In the late classical period, Christians used to judge one as a pagan if he practiced a ritual sacrifice as in the carnivals.

A pivotal Emperor leading to the Dark Ages was Constantine the Great (272–337), who legalised Christianity in February 313 as a compromise with the rival Emperor Licinius (263–325), authoring the Edict of Milan. The Edict stated that Christians should be allowed to follow their faith without oppression along with all other religions/cults in the Roman Empire. He chose the Greek city Byzantium (later known as Constantinople) as the Capital of the Empire and opened the millenium-lasting Byzantine Empire. Since then, the city was the capital of the East Roman Empire (better known as Byzantium) and the Ottoman Empire, now called Istanbul. The Emperor must have favoured Greece out of all the candidates for the capital. As Yannis Rizos commented, Istanbul in Greek means "To the City", saying that his mother always said 'istanbul' when she went out to Corfu city. Istanbul was The City in the Byzantine Empire.

The Edict of Milan, allowing pagans the same rights as Christians, was allegedly reneged by Licinius, not favouring Christians, in the year 320, and Licinius was made a private man in the great civil war of 324. So, the Christian-prone Constantine convened the first

Council of Nicaea in 325, declaring the Nicene Creed, God the Trinity, and the statement of Christian belief. In contrast to Trinity, the non-trinitarian doctrine Arianism, proposed by Arius (c. 256–336) of Alexandria in Egypt, was made illegal. Since then, Constantine the Great heavily promoted the Christian Church, which even seeded in the High Middle Ages the Papal claim to temporal power based on the forged Donation of Constantine. Constantine ordered Old Saint Peter's Basilica to be built, which took over 30 years to complete. For this, he went to great lengths to erect the basilica on top of St. Peter's resting place, even allowing changes of the initial design of the basilica. He became the patron of Christianity with Licinius absent.

Even before becoming the only Emperor of the whole Roman Empire, Constantine dealt a blow to Donatists, whose doctrine derives the name from the North African bishop Donatus (?–c. 355). Donatism had flourished during the fourth and fifth centuries. It had its roots in the Christian community of the Roman African province (now Algeria and Tunisia), which was ruled by Constantine in 311. Donatism was a heresy leading to a schism in the Church of Carthage from the 4th to the 6th centuries. The Roman governor of North African, lenient to the large Christian minority under his rule throughout the persecutions, was satisfied with Christians handing over their scriptures as a token repudiation of faith. But, when the persecution ended, Christians who handed the holy things over were called traitors by their critic Donatists (who were mainly from the poorer classes). Donatists argued that Christian clergy must be faultless for their ministry to be effective, and their prayers and sacraments to be valid. The Donatists were rigourists, saying that the church must be a church of 'saints' but not 'sinners'. Caecilianus, on the opposite side of Donatists, was archdeacon and then Bishop of Carthage in 313–316. His appointment as Bishop led to the Donatist Controversy of the Late Roman Empire. There were Christian bishops ordained by Donatus during 313 and 316 against the bishops of the Caecilianus party. The North African bishops could not come to terms with this, and the Donatists asked Constantine to act as a judge in the dispute. Three regional Church councils, and another trial before Constantine, all ruled against Donatus and the Donatism movement in North Africa. In 317, Constantine issued an edict to confiscate Donatist church property and to send Donatist clergy into exile.

Even before the Council of Nicaea, Donatists were crushed by Constantine. So, the Nicene Creed dealt mostly with Arianism, a name originating from the Christian presbyterian Arius. Arianism is a non-Trinitarian Christological doctrine which asserts the belief that Jesus Christ is the Son of God who was begotten by God the Father at a point in time, a creature distinct from the Father and is therefore subordinate to him, but the Son is also God, i.e. called God the Son.

Also, he enforced the Nicaea Council's recommendation on prohibiting the celebration of the Lord's Supper on the day before the Jewish Passover, which marked a definite break of Christianity from the Jewish tradition. But, Jews were not considered pagans by his laws. Even though it was made illegal if Christians were affected by Jewish, such as by seeking converts, by attacking other Jews who had converted to Christianity, by owning Christian slaves, or by circumcising their slaves, Jewish clergies were given the same exemptions as Christian clergies.

Even with these strong Evicts of Constantine the Great, Epicureanism had permeated deeply in the public in the late classical period, chiefly because of the Epicurean motive of the *pursuit of happiness.* So, there was a strong need to suppress the pagan belief of Epicureanism.

In the early Byzantine Empire in Alexandria, three or four generations after Constantine, there was an influential and beautiful Hellenistic, Neoplatonist philosopher Hypatia (350–370 ?–415) whose father Theon (c. 335–405) was a mathematician. She used to ride a chariot in the city in a philosopher's cloak *tribon.* In her own lifetime, Hypatia was renowned as a great teacher and a wise counsellor, and many came to her to learn the works of Plato and Aristotle.

As recently as 1996, there was big news about Wiles's proof of Fermat's last theorem that $x^3 + y^3 = z^3$ does not have integer solutions. This equation is a Diophantine equation discussed in

*Arithmetica* authored by Diophantinus (201–215 to 285–299) of Alexandria, about one and half centuries before Hypatia. In 1637, Pierre de Fermat wrote in the margin of a copy of *Arithmetica* that he found a truly marvellous proof of his last theorem, but that the proof was too large to fit in the margin. Hypatia is known to have written a commentary on Diophantus's 13-volume *Arithmetica*. This item alone can show that the Neoplatonist Hypatia was an influential mathematician, astronomer, and philosopher. But, in her lifetime, Neoplatonism was not embraced by Christianity. During the religious feud in Alexandria, four generations after the Nicene Creed, Serapeon (the temple of Greek–Egyptian Jupiter as a means to unify the Greeks and Egyptians) was destroyed. The Serapeon in Alexandria had the second-best collection compared to the Museum of Alexandria, containing a half million papyrus rolls in its peak. With the Serapeon gone, the written pagan knowledge also disappeared. During this chaos, Hypatia was murdered by a mob of Christians led by a lector named Peter in March 415. Hypatia's murder shocked the Empire and transformed her into a "martyr for philosophy", and her father's student Damascius became increasingly fervent in his opposition to Christianity. Damascius (c. 458–after 538), born in Damascus of Syria and known as "the last of the Neoplatonists," was the last scholar of the School of Athens. He was one of the pagan philosophers persecuted by Emperor Justinian I in the early 6th century. Among the disciples of Damascius, the most important are Simplicius who was mentioned as the celebrated commentator on Aristotle in Chapter 1. Some modern scholars consider that the legend of Saint Catherine of Alexandria was probably based on the life and murder of Hypatia, with reversed roles of Christians and pagans after embracing Platonism in Christianity in the Middle Ages. But, Neoplatonists in Alexandria at that time were pagans. In any case, our information on the Greeks' atom has a lineage Democritus–Epicurus–Aristotle–Lucretius–Hypatia–Simplicius.

The downfall of the statue of Serapis at Serapeon of Alexandria in 415 was lamented by poet Palladas as the end of way of life in the Epicurean 'Gardens', and the murder of the intellectual Hypatia was a precursor of the death knell for the whole pagan tradition, which was finally terminated by Emperor Justinian in 429. With the Eviction, other paganisms, including Stoicism and Scepticism, were also driven out. Stoicism was started by Zeno of Citium (c. 334 BC–c. 262 BC) in Athens in the early 3rd century BC, and the Stoics were taught that "virtue is the only good" for human beings, and that external thing — such as health, wealth, and pleasure — were not good or bad in themselves. According to Stoicism, the path to happiness for humans is found in accepting the moment as it presents itself, by not allowing oneself to be controlled by the desire for pleasure or fear of pain, exactly the opposite way of Epicureanism. As Neoplatonism was evicted, so was Stoicism. The virtue of Stoicism is similar to that of Platonism, and the stoic attitude was installed in the monasteries in the Middle Age. Scepticism is an attitude where one shows doubt whether something is true or useful. Radical forms of scepticism deny that knowledge or rational belief is possible, and urge us to suspend judgment on many or all controversial matters. More moderate forms of skepticism claim only that nothing can be known with certainty, or that we can know little or nothing about the big question in life, such as whether God exists or whether there is an afterlife. Religious scepticism is "doubt concerning basic religious principles such as immortality, providence, and revelation". The 13th-century saint Thomas Aquinas (1225–1274) stated on the creation in *Genesis*: "With respect to the origin of the world, there is one point that is of the substance of the faith, viz. to know that it began by creation," and the Roman Catholic Catechism[3] published in 1566 placed "belief" in the first place. Scepticism was evicted along with the other paganisms in 429.

Along with Epicureanism, Neoplatonism, Stoicism, and Scepticism, Totemism and Animism also belonged to the evicted paganisms. Along with Animism, Totemism was the earliest form of belief worshipping a sacred object, or symbol that served as an emblem of a group of people, such as a family, clan, lineage, or tribe. Animism derived from Latin *anima* (meaning breath, spirit, and life)

[3]S. M. Barr, *Modern Physics and Ancient Faith* (University of Notre Dame Press, Notre Dame, IN, 2003).

is the religious belief that objects, places, and creatures all possess a distinct spiritual essence. There is some common ground in Totemism and Animism.

By the early 5th century, what mattered most were the logical philosophies from the classical Greek period. Stoicism was practiced by monks in the monasteries sprawling after the Justinian Evict. Thus, as in most cases — Heaven and Hell, Sun and Moon, North and South, plus and minus, good and bad, love and hate, freedom vs. equality, Republican vs. Democrat, particle and wave — there remain two dominating pagans from Greek philosophies: Epicureanism and Neoplatonism. As John Vergados commented, Romans the excellent soldiers wanted some philosophy from Ancient Greeks.

Epicureanism aims at the *pursuit of happiness*, and Neoplatonism aims at the *pursuit of virtue*. Which was chosen by Romans?

Cicero's epigram *nihil est virtute pulchrius* (there is nothing more beautiful than virtue) morally resonates in our ears, and Thomas Jefferson's insertion "pursuit of happiness" in the Declaration of Independence is recited over and over again. It must have been difficult to favour one over the other. To Christians, both were pagans. Then, they looked for a possibility of changing the way of practicing. To Epicureans, all were materialistic and God was not acceptable by definition. They did not view the world in the way of Empedocles that even if gods existed they do not interfere the humans. Epicureans were useless to Christians.

In the 5th century, the greatest Christian Father Saint Augustine (354–430) adopted a very non-literal approach for the '6 days' of creation (*Hexahemeron* in Greek) of *Genesis*, saying that it was not a temporal succession, but all things were produced simultaneously by God in the single instant and subsequently underwent some natural process of development.[4] The 13th century book *Summa* by Saint Thomas Aquinas of the classics of the history of philosophy stated that St. Clement (c. 150–216) and Origen (c. 185–254) had held

[4]S. M. Barr, *Modern Physics and Ancient Faith* (University of Notre Dame Press, Notre Dame, IN, 2003).

the same view.[5] This view held that the universe underwent some natural process of development. But, *hexahemeron* at an instant is not reconcilable with the swerve (little by little) of atomistic creation mused by Lucretius. Platonic creation by *Dẽmiourgos* narrated by Timaeus is not the interpretation of Augustine, but there is a possibility to change the Neoplatonists' minds because they were not 100 % materialist. They had the *virtue* which can be God's will instead of materialistic *happiness.* They can be transformed to Christians. So, through Saint Augustine, Christian Fathers adopted one philosophy of Ancient Greeks, Neoplatonism.

Independently from Saint Augustine, Saint Ambrosius (340–397), Archbishop of Milan, authored the Hexahemeron. Hexahemeron was first presented in Lenten lectures by Saint Basil (329–330 to 379), the bishop of Caesarea Mazaca in Cappadocia (modern-day Turkey). Saint Ambrosius was exchanging letters with Basil and must have been influenced by Basil, and he was notable for his influence on Augustine of Hippo. The *hexahemeron* must have been an issue in the beginning of the 5th century.

There was no place to talk about Epicureanism after 429. And, Epicureanism was forgotten together with the Lucretius poem *De Rerum Natura.*

Scientifically, the Latin numerals are not helpful in developing science by estimating the magnitude of some number. In a sense, the Dark Ages helped in importing the so-called Arabic numerals into Europe in the Islamic era, which began in 622 when Islamic armies started to conquer Arabia, Egypt, and Mesopotamia. In a century, Islam had reached the area of present-day Portugal in the west and Central Asia in the east. The spread of Islam across Western Asia and North Africa encouraged an unprecedented growth in trade and travel by land and sea as far away as Southeast Asia and China. Its Golden Age was roughly between 786 and 1258 (the year Baghdad fell to the Mongols) with stable political structures and flourishing trade.

[5]The views of the church fathers of *Hexahemeron* are reviewed in Appendix 7 of Volume X of the Blackfriars edition of *The Summa Theologiae of St. Thomas Aquinas* (Eyre and Spottiswoode, Ltd., London, 1967), pp. 203–204.

In this Golden age, of course astronomy was useful for determining the Qibla, the direction that should be faced towards Mecca in which to pray. Arabian merchants traded merchandise all over the world to India, to Indonesia, and even to the Far East. During this period, Catholic Europeans got the Oriental spices and also the Indian numerals through Arabian merchants.

Richard Bulliet, Pamela Crossley, Daniel Headrick, Steven Hirsch, and Lyman Johnson state, "Indian mathematicians invented the concept of zero and developed the 'Arabic' numerals and system of *place-value* notation used in most parts of the world today".[6] The development to the currently used numerals was gradual, and the Arabian merchants used it for trading during the third Islamic caliphate, the Abbasid Caliphate (Capital Bagdad, 750–1258), and most Europeans must have thus learned the Arabic numerals.

According to the ancient Indian mathematical text found in 1881 in the village of Bakhshali, Mardan (near Peshawar in present-day Pakistan), the Indian numerals was used around 385 and 465, the estimate given by the carbon dating of Maan Singh.[7] The Bakhshali manuscript, Fig. 1(a), contains the "placing symbol" (a bullet) in the second line from the bottom. In Fig. 1(b), the "placing symbol"

(a)

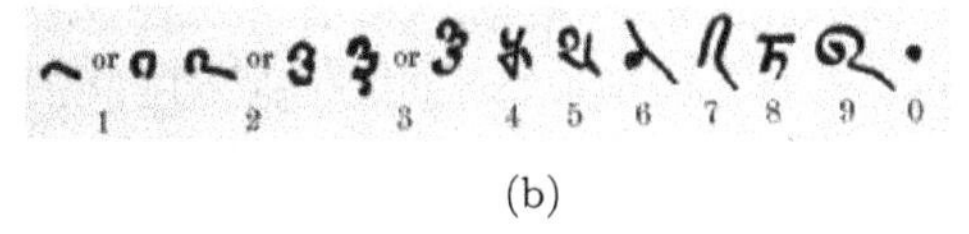


(b)

Figure 1: The Bakhshali manuscript marked on birch bark (a), and the Indian numerals (b).

[6]R. Bulliet, P. Crossley, D. Headrick, S. Hirsch, and L. Johnson, *The Earth and Its Peoples: A Global History*, 3rd Ed. (Houghton Mufflin, Boston, 2005), Chapter 6 "India and Southwest Asia", p. 163, ISBN 0-618-42770-8.
[7]M. Singh, *Subandhu* (Sahitya Akademi, 1993), pp. 9–11, ISBN 81-7201-509-7.

is written as 0. Here, two aspects are of concern in mathematics. First of all the beautiful Arabic numeral itself is not important. The important thing is that it is just one connected letter. As shown in Fig. 1(b), some original Indian numeral forms survive until now but the important aspect of it is just one unit. It is not so in Chinese and in Latin. The second is the placing mark, the bullet in Fig. 1. The placing mark is very useful in the present-day decimal system. It is also useful in binary numbering or in any other numbering system. If we used the duodecimal numbering system, we must have used two more one-unit characters for 10 and 11. The placing can still be the bullet. Today, the decimal-system numerals 1, 2, 3, 4, 5, 6, 7, 8, 9, 0 are used more often than the Roman alphabets. The book *On the Calculation with Hindu Numerals* by al-Khwarizmi (c. 780–850) written about 820 and the book *On the Use of the Indian Numerals* by al-Kindi (801–873) were principally responsible for spreading the Hindu–Arabic numeral system throughout the Middle East and Europe.

In particular, al-Kindi was an Arab Muslim philosopher, deeply affected by the Greek Neoplatonist, and one of his lifelong efforts was to make the Greek thought acceptable to a Muslim audience, which was carried out at the *House of Wisdom* in Baghdad, an institute of translation and learning patronised by the Abbasid Caliphs. Like Simplicius, he was a prodigious writer, writing at least 260 books on geometry (32 books), medicine and philosophy (22 books each), logic (nine books), and physics (12 books).

While Christians in Europe were blocked from the knowledge of the ancient Greeks, al-Kindi spread the Greek view of the solar system from Ptolemy, who placed the Earth at the centre of a series of concentric spheres, in which the known heavenly bodies (the Moon, Mercury, Venus, the Sun, Mars, Jupiter, and the stars) are embedded, which would be changed by Copernicus after the Dark Ages of the Europe. Al-Kindi must have been influenced by Saint Augustine (354–430) in attempting to demonstrate the compatibility between philosophy and natural theology, and had successfully incorporated Aristotelian and (especially) Neoplatonist thought into an Islamic philosophical framework as the first philosopher writing in the Arabic language. Most medieval Islamic mathematicians wrote in Arabic with some others writing in Persian.

In al-Kindi's view, the knowledge of God is the goal of metaphysics, but later the most influential Islamic philosopher al-Farabi (c. 872 to 950–951) strongly disagreed with him on this issue, saying that metaphysics is actually concerned with the first principle, and as such, the nature of God is purely incidental. A first principle is a basic proposition or assumption that cannot be deduced from any other proposition or assumption. In philosophy, first principles are from First Cause attitudes taught by Aristotelians. In mathematics, first principles are referred to as axioms or postulates. In physics, theoretical work is said to be from first principles or *ab initio*, if it does not make assumptions such as an empirical model and a parameter fitting. In the West, several centuries after al-Farabi, René Descartes (1596–1650) described the concept of a first principle in the preface to the "Principles of Philosophy: Now these principles must possess two conditions: in the first place, they must be so clear and evident that the human mind, when it attentively considers them, cannot doubt of their truth; in the second place, the knowledge of other things must be so dependent on them as that though the principles themselves may indeed be known apart from what depends on them, the latter cannot nevertheless be known apart from the former." Central to al-Kindi's understanding of metaphysics is God's absolute oneness, which he considered an attribute uniquely associated with God. In addition to absolute oneness, al-Kindi also described God as the Creator or an active agent. Of God as the agent, all other intermediary agencies are contingent upon Him. The key idea here is that God 'acts' through created intermediaries, which in turn 'act' on one another — through a chain of cause and effect — to produce the desired result. In reality, these intermediary agents do not 'act' at all; they are merely a conduit for God's own action.

In contrast to al-Kindi, who considered the subject of metaphysics to be God, al-Farabi believed that it is related to God only to the extent that God is a principle of absolute being. Al-Kindi's view was, however, a common misconception regarding Greek philosophy among Muslim intellectuals at his time in Baghdad, and it was for this reason that Avicenna (c. 980–1037) remarked that he did not understand Aristotle's metaphysics properly until he had read a prolegomenon written by al-Farabi. Neoplatonism was started in the Platonic tradition by Plotinus (c. 204–205 to 270) in Hellenistic Roman Egypt. Hypatia mentioned earlier was a Neoplatonist. His six *Enneads* were edited and compiled by his student Porphyry (c. 234–305) around 270. Through Augustine of Hippo (354–430), an early Christian theologian, the Cappadocian Fathers, Pseudo-Dionysius the Areopagite (a Christian theologian and philosopher of the late 5th to early 6th century), and several subsequent Christian and Muslim thinkers, *Enneads* greatly influenced Western and Near-Eastern thought. Neoplatonism influenced mainstream theological concepts within religions, such as the work on duality of the one in two metaphysical states that laid the foundation for Christian notions of Jesus being both god and man, a foundational idea in Christian theology.

Al-Farabi's cosmology is essentially based upon three pillars: Aristotelian metaphysics of causation, highly developed Plotinian cosmology, and the Ptolemaic astronomy. In his model, the universe is viewed as a number of concentric circles: the outermost sphere or 'first heaven', the sphere of fixed stars, Saturn, Jupiter, Mars, the Sun, Venus, Mercury, and finally the Moon. The centre of these concentric circles inside the Moon's orbit contains the material world. It is a more elaborate form of Fig. 5 in Chapter 1.

In the Dark Ages, both Christian Fathers and Muslim philosophers were concerned about the role of God and the creation of the universe, and accepted the concept of "duality". Contemporary physicists also use that word: wave–particle duality in Bohr's quantum mechanics, "triality" as an extended form in the heyday of the eight-fold way, and T–S duality and ADS/CFT correspondence in string theory. Among these usages, the most profound one is the wave–particle duality that is discussed in Chapter 5.

In the Islamic world, some aspects of fundamentals of mechanics were also studied, which is however dwarfed by Newtonian mechanics and universal gravitation. In the 6th century, John Philoponus (c. 490–570) rejected the Aristotelian view of motion. However, unlike

Galileo, Philoponus did not have the unfortunate peril of sitting in front of inquisitors. He argued instead that an object acquires an inclination to move when it has a motive power impressed on it. More interesting is the statement of Ibn Sina (980–1037) that a moving object has "force" which is dissipated by external agents like air resistance. Ibn Sina distinguished between 'force' and 'inclination' (mayl); he claimed that an object gained mayl when the object is in opposition to its natural motion. His mayl is potential energy under current understanding. But, he did not invent an appropriate device to prove his statement.

In the Islamic world, there was great progress in practical applications, e.g. in geology, astronomy, and engineering. As mentioned above, astronomy became a major discipline within Islamic science. Another was astrology, predicting events with the best knowledge for going to war or founding a city. Al-Battani (850–922) accurately determined the length of the solar year. He contributed to the Tables of Toledo, used by astronomers to predict the movements of the Sun, Moon, and planets. Six centuries later, Copernicus (1473–1543) used these astronomic tables. Al-Zarqali (1028–1087) developed a more accurate astrolabe, used for centuries afterward. He constructed a water clock in Toledo, and discovered that the Sun's apogee moves slowly relative to the fixed stars, and obtained a good estimate of its motion by its rate of change. Nasir al-Din Tusi (1201–1274) in Persia wrote an important revision to Ptolemy's 2nd-century celestial model. When Tusi became Helagu's astrologer, he was given an observatory and gained access to Chinese techniques and observations. He developed trigonometry as a separate field, and compiled the most accurate astronomical tables available at that time.

But, the historian of science Bertrand Russell took the view[8] that Islamic science lacked the intellectual energy required for innovation, and was chiefly important for preserving ancient knowledge and handing it on to medieval Europe, while admirable in many technical

[8]B. Russell, *History of Western Philosophy* (Simon and Shuster, US, 1945), Book 2, Part 2, Chapter X.

ways. Transfer of Indian/Arabic numerals to medieval Europe may be his basis of judgement, but al-Farabi's understanding of Aristotle is a fundamental intellectual understanding. So, recently, there has been a revisionist view, exemplified by theoretical physicist Nobel Laureate Abdus Salam,[9] George Saliba,[10] and John M. Hobson,[11] that a Muslim scientific revolution occurred during the Middle Ages. Scholars such as Donald Routledge Hill[12] and Ahmad Y. Hassan[13] argue that Islam was the driving force behind these scientific achievements. Here, it is worthwhile to cite Gustavo Branco's comment[14] that in recent years physics in the Mediterranean region was not as progressive as that in the Nothern Europe because of the influence of the Catholicism forbidding free thinking. In a sense, Hill and Hassan point out that in the Islamic world there was not that much prohibition of free thinking.

[9] A. Salam, H. R. Dalafi, and M. Hassan (1994). *Renaissance of Sciences in Islamic Countries* (World Scientific, Singapore, 1994), p. 162, ISBN 9971-5-0713-7.

[10] G. Saliba, *A History of Arabic Astronomy: Planetary Theories During the Golden Age of Islam* (New York University Press, 1994), ISBN 978-0-8147-8023-7.

[11] J. M. Hobson, *The Eastern Origins of Western Civilisation* (Cambridge University Press, 2004, ISBN 978-0-521-54724-6).

[12] D. R. Hill, *Islamic Science and Engineering* (Edinburgh University Press, 1993), ISBN 978-0-7486-0455-5.

[13] A. Y. Hassan and D. R. Hill, *Islamic Technology: An Illustrated History* (Cambridge University Press, 1986), p. 282.

[14] A private comment at Corfu, Summer 2019.

# Chapter 3

# Renaissance

In science, Sir Isaac Newton, who is discussed in greater detail in Chapter 4, was the giant in the Enlightenment period succeeding the Italian Renaissance. In Europe, the Renaissance was an important event that stretched from the late 14th century to the 17th century in Rome and especially in Florence, preceded by the Middle Ages, with brief periods of Carolingian and Ottonian Renaissances in the northwest. In historical terms, the Renaissance is important because it led to a major shift in the cosmic view of the universe from the Ptolemaic to Copernican. The Renaissance is considered to have begun in the city-states of the Italian peninsula, Genoa, Florence, Milan, Naples, Rome, and Venice. Poggio's finding of the poem *On the Nature of Things* in 1417 happened in the early period, practically ending the Dark Ages. Poggio (1380–1459) was born 6 years after Petrarch's death. Francesco Petrarca (1304–1374), or simply called Petrarch, became the second poet laureate on April 8, 1341 since antiquity and was one of the earliest humanists in the Italian Renaissance. Petrarch's rediscovery of Cicero's letters is considered the initiation of the Renaissance, beginning with his search for classical Latin poems. Petrarch was a devout Catholic and commented that God had given humans their vast intellectual and creative potential to be used to their fullest, which is accepted by many current scientists also including the authors. But, the poem *On the Nature of Things* does not place God anywhere in the universe.

An opening of the scientific renaissance was by Nicolas Copernicus (1473–1543), a Polish astronomer who published *Da Revolutionibus Orbium Celestium*, or Rotations of the Celestial Spheres, just before his death in 1543. In it, he favoured a heliocentric view of the Solar System. It is generally thought that Copernicus was ignorant of a similar view by Aristarchus of Samos (c. 310–230 BC), 1800 years earlier, who put the planets in their correct order of distance around the central fire, the Sun.

The Copernican view, even extending to a principle in cosmology, was accepted a generation later by the Neoplatonist Giordano Bruno (1548–1600). Bruno was a cosmological theorist who extended the Copernican principle outside the Solar system. Stars are distant suns like our Sun and have their own planets. Even he raised the possibility that these planets might foster life of their own, a philosophical position known as cosmic pluralism. He also insisted that the universe is infinite and could have no "centre". These views are taken by most 21-century cosmologists. But, he had to sit in front of Roman Catholic Inquisitors under the peril of death, unlike Galileo, because of his religious views. There was a Danish astronomer Tycho Brahé (1546–1601), a contemporary of Bruno, known for his accurate and comprehensive astronomical and planetary observations. His observations were some five times more accurate than the best available observations at the time. In an essay, Burtt wrote in the early 20th century that Brahé was "the first competent mind in modern astronomy to feel ardently the passion for exact empirical facts," which was adopted by Galileo by actively making devices to check the empirical facts. As an astronomer, Brahé worked to combine what he saw as the geometrical benefits of the Copernican system with the philosophical benefits of the Ptolemaic system into his own model of the universe, the Tychonic system, of which the philosophy interference went against his own passion for empirical importance.

A scientist of paramount importance in the Renaissance was Galileo Galilei (1564–1642), who is often called the father of modern science. A generation later than Bruno, he was born in Pisa, and moved to Florence at the age of eight. He studied speed and velocity of particles, and their free fall under gravity. In particular, he famously observed the pendulum formed by a chandelier hanging in the Pisa Cathedral (still there today) and found that its period was independent of its amplitude, thereby confirming the constancy of gravitational acceleration. It may be an apocryphal story that he dropped unequal masses from the Leaning Tower of Pisa and showed that they fell with the same acceleration. This refuted the philosophical speculation by Aristotle that heavier objects fell more quickly. This underlines why Galileo is rightfully regarded as the father of the scientific method, that theory must be tested by experiment and observation.

In 1610, Galileo acquired a telescope and discovered four moons of Jupiter, the rings of Saturn, and sunspots. It must have been a thrill to him to find four moons on a line in the sky, resulting in deep questions on the geometry of the rotating moons and hence the geometry of the rotating planets. This was possible by increasing the potential of observation by the new telescope. Galileo's support for the heliocentric Solar System, as confirmed by his observation, landed him in trouble with the Catholic Church and their Inquisition convicted him of heresy for saying the Earth moved, in contradiction to the Tychonic system adopted from teaching of Ptolemy. He was sentenced to house arrest for the rest of his life.

Nevertheless, despite the myopia of the Catholics, Galileo occupies a unique stature in the scientific renaissance.

Observational astronomy was developed by followers of Tycho Brahé. Brahé was generously supported by the King of Denmark, who gave him an island (Hven) and observatory (Uraniborg) at a cost of about 10% of the the Danish national budget, said to be the best-funded scientific research in history. Tycho preceded the telescope and used huge naked-eye sextants to obtain data of unprecedented accuracy on the movements of the stars and especially the planets.

When the King died, however, his son, not sharing his father's obsession, proposed a major cut in Tycho's funding. Not one to take a demotion, he decided to move and become the Imperial Astronomer in Prague, Austria, working closely not with a mere King but with an

Emperor. He famously had a false nose, thought to have been made of gold, while he was alive. He died in a remarkable manner at a dinner hosted by the Emperor. He desperately needed to urinate but could not stand up before the Emperor did and died of a burst bladder. This fate has been confirmed after exhumation of his body, which, however, discovered that the celebrated nose had actually been made of brass, not gold.

In Prague, the immediate predecessor of Newton arrived. Johannes Kepler (1571–1630) became an assistant to Tycho Brahé in Prague, then Imperial Mathematician to the Emperor. He was a corresponding member of the Accademia dei Lincei in Rome.

Kepler studied the data on planetary orbits and arrived at his celebrated three laws of planetary motion. The first law states that the orbits are ellipses with the Sun at a focus. The second states that a radius vector sweeps out equal areas in equal times. The third law, states that the orbital periods of the different planets are proportional to the major axis raised to the power 3/2.

The first two laws were enunciated by Kepler relatively quickly. They show that the force is central and conserves angular momentum as expected. It took Kepler twenty more years to find his third law, which is the only one which relates the different planets. This law shows that the force must diminish like the inverse square of the separation.

Kepler's laws of planetary motion played an important role in the discovery of the Universal Law of Gravitation. This would require the appearance in England of a third genius, this time in physics, comparable in impact to Darwin in biology or Shakespeare in English literature. His name was Isaac Newton (1642–1727) who was born 100 miles from Kidderminster.

Returning to Copernicus (1473–1543), he was born and died in Royal Prussia, Poland. He was a polymath, known not only for heliocentrism but also for the theory of the quantity of money, including what is called Gresham's Law attributed to Sir Thomas Gresham (1519–1579) that *bad money drives out good.* Bad money means money worth in commodity value less than its face value.

Copernicus was educated and taught in Italy, in Bologna (1496–1500), Padua (1501–1503), and Ferrara (1503). His heliocentric theory is thought to be independent of that of Aristarchus (300 BC–230 BC).

He was born into a patrician and wealthy family, and could speak Latin, German, Polish, Greek, Italian, and Hebrew. His science was written in Latin. Copernicus is the modern spelling of a name that was recorded at various times as Kopernik, Copernik, or Koppernigk.

Copernicus's father died in 1483 when he was 10 years old, whereupon his maternal uncle Lucas Watzenrode (1447–1512) looked after his education and career. In 1491, Copernicus matriculated at the University of Krakow (now Jagiellonian University) where he studied philosophy and astronomy until 1495. He collected a large library of astronomy, now held at Uppsala University Library. While a student, Copernicus initiated his analysis of the contradictions in the conventional wisdom of astronomy based on Aristotle's homocentric spheres and Ptolemy's system of epicycles.

By 1495, his uncle became a bishop and tried to place his nephew, Copernicus, into an ecclesiastical post. Instead, he went to Bologna to study canon law, although he continued his passion for astronomy. He stayed in Bologna studying medicine until 1500 when he moved to Padua, then briefly to Ferrara. By age 30 in 1503, he moved permanently back to Poland where he stayed for his remaining 40 years.

Before 1514, he wrote a preliminary version of his heliocentric theory, called *Commentariolis*. This had very limited circulation, although Tycho Brahé later included a fragment of it in his treatise.

In 1514, Copernicus began making astronomical observations, especially of the Sun, Moon, Mars, and Saturn. By 1533, 10 years before his death, Copernicus had essentially completed *De Revolutionibus Orbium Celestium*, but held it back from publication because he feared criticism of his novel and "incomprehensible" ideas.

He received the final printed pages of his masterpiece on the day he died, so could bid farewell to his lifework. He placed the Sun at the centre of the Solar System, then correctly ordered the six known planets Mercury, Venus, Earth, Mars, Jupiter, and Saturn. So far, so good, but then he decided that the fixed stars were in an orbit around the Sun somewhat outside that of Saturn!

Galileo Galilei was born in Pisa in 1564 and died in Arcetri, near Florence, in 1642. Appropriately, there is now a Galileo Galilei Institute of Theoretical Physics in Arcetri, founded in 2005. He was buried in the Basilica of Santa Croce in Florence and remembered variously as the father of modern physics, of the scientific method, or of modern science.

Galileo studied speed and velocity, gravity and free fall, pendula, the telescope, the phases of Venus (important in refuting the geocentric model), the four largest satellites of Jupiter, Saturn's rings, and sunspots. He championed the heliocentric theory, but this was met with opposition from astronomers.

The Roman Inquisition investigated him in 1615 and concluded that heliocentrism was "foolish and absurd in philosophy" and "contradicts the sense of Holy Scripture," and hence was heretical.

In 1632, Galileo published *Dialogue Concerning the Two Chief World Systems*, which, as we shall see later, made his situation worse, alienating the Pope and the Jesuits. Tried by the Inquisition, he was forced to recant and spend the rest of his life under house arrest.

As a boy, Galileo became an accomplished lutenist, taught by his father who also inculcated a scepticism for established authority and a passion for the combination of mathematics and experiments.

He considered becoming a priest, but instead in 1580 he enrolled in the University of Pisa to study medicine. In 1581, he observed the swinging candelabra in the Pisa Cathedral (it is still there). Air currents changed the amplitudes of the swings, but, timing it with his pulse, he noticed that the period did not change. He checked on this by observing two pendulums at home. He stayed away from mathematics because a physician earned more than a mathematician.

He created a thermoscope, precursor of a thermometer, and invented a hydrostatic balance. Due to these inventions, he got an academic position in Florence. By 1589, he became the Chair of mathematics in Pisa and in 1592 moved to Padua to teach geometry, mechanics, and astronomy until 1610.

He studied the tides as evidence for the Copernican system, although his theory was incorrect, being based on the rotation of the Earth. His contemporary Kepler knew the tides were caused by the Moon, giving two (not one) high tides per day. Galileo showed no interest in this theory by Kepler, nor, surprisingly, in Kepler's elliptic orbits for the planets.

Galileo published *Il Saggiatore* about comets and about how science should be practiced in 1623. This book was dedicated to, and pleased, Pope Urban VIII, but it led to a controversy with a Jesuit astronomer, Orazio Grassi (1583–1654), who wrongly thought that comets move on a circle at a constant radius from the Earth.

Tycho Brahé opposed heliocentrism because of the failure to detect the annual stellar parallax, but it is now known that such parallax is extremely small because of the distance to the stars. One parsec is defined to be the distance from the Sun at which the Earth's orbit subtends one arc second, and the stars' distance is measured in parsecs. If they were comparably as close as Saturn, as drawn on Copernicus' diagrams, there would be many arc minutes of parallax which could be measured even then.

Religious opposition to heliocentrism arose from its apparent contradiction to certain passages in the Bible, most notably the following ones:

> Psalms **96:**10.
> *The world also is established. It cannot be moved.*
>
> Psalms **104:**5.
> *The Lord laid the foundations of the Earth, that it should not be moved forever.*
>
> Ecclesiastes **1:**5.
> *The Sun also rises, then the Sun goes down, and hurries to its place where it rises.*

By 1615, Galileo's writings had been submitted to the Roman Inquisition by Father Niccolo Lorini via Cardinal Paolo Camilla Frondati. The claim was that Galileo was trying to reinterpret the Bible in violation of the Council of Trent, which appeared to be like

Protestantism. Interestingly, as a scientific basis, the incorrect ideas of Tycho Brahé were used. These machinations against Galileo had the backing of the Archbishop of Florence, Alessandro Marzimedici (1563–1630).

In 1616, Pope Paul V instructed Cardinal Bellarmin (1542–1621), who was later canonised in 1930 to become St. Robert Bellarmine, to deliver the Vatican's finding that heliocentrism is false to Galileo, ordering Galileo to abandon his opinion that the Sun is still and the Earth moves. Galileo was not to hold, teach, or defend heliocentrism either orally or in writing. At the same time, Copernicus's famous 1543 masterpiece *De Revolutionibus Orbium Celestium* was to be banned until it could be "corrected".

From 1616 to 1633, Galileo wisely stayed away from the controversy. Meanwhile, in 1623, Cardinal Maffeo Barberini, a friend and admirer of Galileo, became Pope Urban VIII. He had opposed the condemnation by his predecessor.

In 1632, with formal papal and inquisition permission, Galileo published *Dialogue Concerning the Two Chief World Systems*, which presented both the geocentrism of Ptolemy and the heliocentrism of Copernicus.

However, in the *Dialogue*, the geocentric view is presented by a character named Simplico with a connotation in Italian of a simpleton, so the book appeared to strongly advocate the Copernican and therefore "heretical" view. Whether Galileo was malicious or merely politically naïve is not clear, but he thereby succeeded in alienating his biggest and most powerful supporter, Pope Urban VIII.

Not surprisingly, the Pope summoned Galileo to Rome where he appeared before the Inquisitor, Father Vincenzo Maculani (1578–1667), known to be severe and harsh, four times during 1633. The Pope wanted to know Galileo's intention in writing his *Dialogue* and authorised Maculani to use torture if necessary. However, Maculani decided that Galileo was too old and too ill to undergo such abuse.

In June 1633, the Inquisition sentenced him as follows:

(i) He was forced to recant.
(ii) He was to remain under house arrest *for the rest of his life.*

(iii) The *Dialogue* was banned as was any future publication by Galileo.

It is claimed that when he recanted, Galileo said under his breath *E pur si muove* (And yet it moves).

Galileo was eventually allowed to return to his villa *Il Gioiello* at Acetri, just South of Florence, where he died on January 8, 1642. The Pope opposed his immediate burial in the Basilica of Santa Croce, but he was reburied there in 1737 with an impressive monument in his honour. One of his fingers was removed and is on display at the *Museo Galileo* in Florence.

Among his scientific contributions, Galileo famously stated that the Laws of Nature are mathematical: *The Universe is written in the language of mathematics*. This had not been obvious previously. He separated science from both philosophy and religion, which was another first. He also understood the relationship between mathematics, theoretical physics, and experimental physics.

He showed that the trajectory of an artillery shell, neglecting air resistance, is a parabola.

He made telescopes with up to 30× magnification and sold them to merchants and sailors. In March 1610, he published *Sidereus Nuncius* (*Starry Messenger*) about his telescopic astronomical observations.

In 1610, he at first thought the satellites of Jupiter were fixed stars lying on a straight line through the planet. He found three on January 7th and a fourth on January 13th. On subsequent nights, however, the "stars" moved and disappeared by being hidden behind Jupiter. He called them the Medician stars in honour of his future patron Cosimo II de Medici, the Grand Duke of Tuscany.

The four satellites were independently discovered by Simon Marius who gave them their names Io, Europa, Ganymede, and Callisto in his book *Mundus Iovialis* (1614).

These satellites clearly violated the geocentric theory. By 1611, Galileo had obtained impressively accurate measurements of their periods.

By observing the full set of phases for the Sun's illumination of Venus, he made the geocentric model untenable and it was fatal for

Ptolemy's theory. He was confused by Saturn's rings when viewed from different angles and thought wrongly that they might be stars. He observed sunspots both by telescope and the naked eye and noted an annual variation.

In 1609, Galileo had studied the Moon with a telescope and discovered the lunar mountains and craters. They had been seen 4 months earlier by the English mathematician Thomas Harriot.

In the direction of Engineering, Galileo manufactured geometric and military compasses. He made thermometers.

He constructed a reflecting telescope. The word "telescope" was coined by Giovanni Demisiani in 1611 at a banquet where Galileo was inducted as member of the Accademia dei Lincei. Later, the Linceans also coined "microscope" when a variant of his instrument was directed at insects.

In physics, Galileo provided a precursor of the classical mechanics of Newton. He showed that pendula are isochronous, initially by seeing the chandelier in the Pisa Cathedral and timing the swings using his pulse.

He tried unsuccessfully to measure the speed of light using lanterns separated by about a mile. Of course, he could find only a lower limit on $c$. Nevertheless, he did realise that coordinate systems moving with constant relative velocity are equivalent so that absolute motion, including absolute rest, does not exist. This Galilean Invariance provided a basis for Newton's and Einstein's later frameworks.

Aristotle had taught that heavier objects fall faster, proportional to their weight. Galileo is reputed to have dropped unequal weights from the Leaning Tower in Pisa but this may be apocryphal. Such an experiment was done using the church tower in Delft, by de Groot and Stevinus. Most experiments were done using inclined planes, examples of which can be viewed at the *Museo Galileo* in Florence.

The fact that objects of different weights fall at the same speed had been known to John Philoponus (c. 490–570) of Alexandria in the 6th century AD. Galileo knew of Philoponus's work.

Galileo knew that the distance a body fell without air resistance goes quadratically with time. He grasped the idea of inertia, which became Newton's 1st Law, in contradiction with Aristotle who believed that a body would remain in motion only by the action of a force. Philoponus had also realised this error by Aristotle. Kepler's inability to understand inertia is why he never formulated the law of universal gravity.

Clearly, Galileo was a polymath just like Copernicus before him. However, he was not a great mathematician and made mistakes, e.g. he thought that infinite numbers cannot be compared, an idea contradicted in later work by Georg Cantor (1845–1918).

Posthumously, the Catholic church backpedalled on its unfair treatment of Galileo. In 1718, everything except the *Dialogue* was permitted to be published. In 1741, Pope Benedict XIV authorised publication of Galileo's complete works. In 1992, Pope John Paul II expressed official regret about Galileo.

Asteroid 697 Galilea is named in his honour.

Tycho Brahé (1546–1601) was a Danish nobleman. He was an exceptionally good observational astronomer, finding results that were five times more accurate than the best available ones.

His Tychonic system had the Moon orbiting the Earth and the planets orbiting the Sun (both correct), but incorrectly had the Sun orbiting the Earth, in a hybrid geo-heliocentric system.

He was the eldest son of a noble Danish family and as such appeared destined for the natural patrician occupations of hunting and warfare. But, he had an uncle Joergen who was a country squire and vice-admiral who was more educated and childless.

Tycho's father agreed with Joergen before Tycho was born that, if Tycho was a boy, the uncle could adopt and raise him. He changed his mind and reneged. When a younger brother was born, however, Joergen kidnapped Tycho. The father threatened to murder Joergen, but eventually calmed down especially because Tycho would inherit a big estate from his uncle.

At age seven, his uncle insisted that Tycho study Latin despite his parents objecting. At the age of 13, he entered the University of Copenhagen to study law and philosophy. At that impressionable age, there was a life-changing event. He experienced a partial eclipse of the Sun which had been precisely predicted. This seemed divine to him, that men should know the movement of the heavenly bodies a long time beforehand and predict their future places and relative positions.

This predictability may have been appealing to him because of the uncertainty in his personal life. Because he was rich, he could immediately buy a copy of *Almagest* by Ptolemy, as well as some astronomical tables which showed the planetary positions at any time.

Ptolemy had made such tables which had been revised by a group of fifty astronomers in Spain in 1252, organised by Alfonso X of Castile. They were called the Alfonsine tables. Tycho also purchased a recent set of tables based on Copernicus' theory.

When he was 16, his uncle sent him to Leipzig in Germany to study law accompanied by a tutor Anders Vedel who was 20 years old and himself became famous later as Denmark's first great historian. The problem for the tutor was that Tycho was obsessed with astronomy and stayed up all night observing the stars.

At age 17, he observed a special celestial event when Jupiter and Saturn passed very close to earth on August 17, 1563. He found that the Alfonsine tables were off by a month in predicting the event and that his Copernican tables were off by a few days. Tycho found this scientific performance by the astronomers to be pathetically inadequate and decided that much better planetary tables could be made by more accurate observations. At age 17, he decided that this would be lifework.

Anders Vedel gave up on trying to tutor him in law although they remained good friends for life. The uncle died of pneumonia after rescuing the King from drowning when the King fell from the bridge to his castle, after returning from a naval battle with the Swedes.

Upon returning to his family in Denmark, he received an unfriendly reception because they despised his stargazing and his neglect for the law. So, Tycho returned to Germany and fell in with some rich amateur astronomers in Augsburg. He persuaded them that what they needed was accurate observation. Since telescopes had not yet been invented, this meant building large quadrants to find lines of sight to the stars.

The group made a big wooden quadrant with a 19-foot radius which took 20 men to set up. It was graduated down to 160°. This quadrant represented the beginning of Tycho's world-changing, accurate astronomical observations.

While he was in Germany, Tycho lost his temper in a quarrel with another student about who was the better mathematician. This led to a sword dual in which part of Tycho's nose was cut off and then replaced by a metal substitute, perhaps of gold and silver. Afterward, he always carried a snuffbox containing something to rub on his nose to keep it stuck together.

At age 26, in 1570, Tycho returned to Denmark and lived for a while with his family, then with his uncle Steen Bille who started the first paper mill and glassworks in Denmark. Steen was the only family member who approved of stargazing.

On November 11, 1572, another astronomical event occurred which was life-changing for Tycho. Walking back from Steen's laboratory, he noticed a new star in the sky brighter than Venus. He called various servants and peasants to confirm that the new star was really there. It lasted 18 months and could be seen in daytime. This is later known as supernova SN1572.

From both a theological view and an astronomical view, the key question was *where* was the new star. If it was in the upper atmosphere, that would be acceptable because at that level there was continuous change. But, if it was in the eighth sphere (after Mercury, Venus, Earth, Mars, Jupiter, Saturn, and Neptune), which was the fixed stars and the edge of heaven, change was impossible because, according to Aristotlian and Christian dogma, this sphere had remained unchanged since the day of creation.

So, the appearance of the supernova seen by Tycho was, for him, a big deal. Using a new sextant with a metallic scale calibrated in arc minutes, far better than any competition, he showed that the new star did not measurably move relative to the fixed stars and *was*, therefore, in the eighth sphere. In 1573, he started writing a book about it until he decided that writing a book was too undignified for a nobleman. The present two authors evidently do not share Tycho's views about dignity. Tycho further refused to give a course about his discovery until the King ordered him to do it.

By this time (1575), Tycho was world-renowned and went on a grand tour to be well received and feted in the major centres. He let it be known that he was seriously considering a move to Basel in Switzerland. King Frederick II was so alarmed by this rumour, especially as his own life had been saved by Tycho's uncle, that he offered a choice of castles in Denmark. This did not work so the King offered a whole Island, flat with white cliffs, about three miles long, called Hveen.

The island is near to Elsinore, which was Hamlet's castle in the Shakespeare play. Denmark would pay for building an observatory and a house, and all the Hveen inhabitants would become Tycho's subjects, as the "King of Hveen". The reason that the king of Denmark, a relatively small country, had so much wealth was that the Protestant Reformation had placed the Church's lands and resources into his hands.

Tycho hired a German architect and built his *Uraniborg* (castle of the heavens) a research institute with large astronomical instruments. It was surrounded by a square wall, 250 feet on a side, and had an onion dome like the Kremlin with an Italian-style facade. There were rooms in *Uraniburg* designed to accommodate his large quadrants, as well as murals, a printing press, and even a prison for troublemaking tenants.

The library of *Uraniborg* contained a five-foot-diameter brass globe specially made for Tycho in Augsburg. The positions of the stars were engraved accurately on it during 25 years of dedicated observation. In Tycho's study, a quadrant was built into the wall itself with a mural of Tycho. The quadrant was centred on an open window through which observations were made. A number of clocks were used simultaneously to time the observations; the observer and timekeeper worked in tandem. There was a large staff and duplicate equipment allowed four independent measurements of everything, greatly reducing the possibility of error. The typical error of Tycho's "predecessor" Ptolemy had been 10 minutes of arc, and now Tycho could always achieve 1 minute of arc.

There were a number of idiosyncratic gadgets such as a system of bells so that he could call every room to summon his assistants. There were many distinguished visitors including princes, courtiers, and King James VI of Scotland. Tycho hosted huge parties and feasts for his visitors, occasionally ordering silence so that everybody could listen to a dwarf called Jepp whom Tycho believed had second sight. He owned a tame elk which died one night after falling down the stairs after imbibing too much beer!

Tycho treated his tenants on the Isle of Hveen abominably and readily threw them into prison if they caused any problem. Tycho's days were numbered, however, because King Ferdinand II, his reliable supporter, died in 1588 of too much drink as discussed at the funeral by the aforementioned Anders Sørensen Vedel (1542–1616) who had once been Tycho's tutor of law.

The problem for Tycho was that the new King was Christian IV, son of Ferdinand II, who wrote several unanswered letters to Tycho. Measures were taken to reduce Tycho's huge income to more normal proportions. Tycho became bored with Hveen and collected together his family, his assistants, and his equipment including Jepp the dwarf and moved around Europe in search of a better place to build an observatory. As for his mobility, Tycho said, "An astronomer must be cosmopolitan, because ignorant statesmen cannot be expected to value their services."

Tycho gave King Christian IV a second chance by writing to him his conditions for re-employment, but the King was not interested. In 1597, 4 years before his death, the new King Christian IV sent Tycho into exile. He was, however, invited by Emperor Rudolph II to Prague and acquired an observatory at Benatky nad Jizerou. In 1599, Tycho arrived with his entourage in Prague where Emperor Rudolph II appointed him *Imperial Mathematicus* with a big salary of 3000 florins per annum, together with the castle of his choice! During his last year, 1600–1601, he was assisted by Johannes Kepler.

After he died, Tycho's body was exhumed twice, in 1901 and 2010, and it was confirmed that he died of a burst bladder while at dinner with the Emperor of Austria after being compelled to stay seated until the Emperor left his seat. It was further established that the artificial nose was made of brass.

Johannes Kepler (1571–1630) was a German mathematician and optician.

He was born on December 27, 1571 as a premature child after a pregnancy lasting 224 days, 9 hours, and 53 minutes. This precise piece of information was provided in Arthur Koestler's book *The Sleepwalkers* (1989). Kepler went on to take astrology, and astronomy, quite seriously.

He was born in Weil in a wine region in Southwest Germany, quite close to France. The Kepler family's situation makes Tycho's family background appear quite tranquil by comparison. Kepler's grandfather was mayor of Weil. Kepler described his grandmother thus: "restless, clever and lying, but devoted to religion; slim and of a fiery nature; vivacious, an inveterate troublemaker; jealous, extreme in her hatreds, violent, a bearer of grudges ... and all her children have something of this."

Kepler described his father thus: "A man vicious, inflexible, quarrelsome and doomed to a bad end. Venus and Mars increase his malice. Saturn in VII made him study gunnery." His mother fares no better: "small, thin, swarthy, gossiping and quarrelsome, of a bad disposition." The mother collected herbs and made potions that she believed had magical powers.

Kepler's mother was raised by an aunt who was burned at the stake as a witch. Kepler had to hire several lawyers to defend his 70-year-old mother from the same fate as she had been incarcerated on a charge of witchcraft when another woman born in the same town as Kepler's mother accused her of complicity, and had already left one of her thumbs stuck in the rack.

When he was a 7-month-old child, Kepler was sickly and contracted smallpox. His vision was very defective and he was constantly ill. He took double the normal time to learn elementary Latin, but did better at high school in Maulbronn at a school which only half a century earlier was haunted by the infamous Dr. Faustus.

Kepler proceeded to the University of Tübingen, a Protestant institution, to study mainly theology and philosophy but also mathematics and astronomy. The Dukes of Württemberg, after becoming Lutheran, put in place a good educational system with support for the poor to ensure they could supply educated priests.

At the Tübingen University, Kepler's exceptional intellect became evident. He admired his astronomy professor Maestlin who taught the Ptolemaic system but personally believed Copernicus. Kepler publicly defended Copernicus in a debate, thus ensuring his failure to acquire a faculty position at Tübingen where he was an alumnus. For example, Luther himself had mocked Copernicus' theory as, he argued, the Bible proved it wrong.

Thus, Kepler instead accepted a professorship in Graz, now in Austria, in 1594. Amusingly, one of his duties was to make astrological predictions. Kepler wrote the following: "a mind accustomed to mathematical deduction, when confronted with the faulty foundations (of astrology) resists a long, long time, like an obstinate mule, until compelled by beating and curses to put its foot into that dirty puddle."

Nevertheless, Kepler was very clever. He went ahead and confidently predicted a cold winter and a Turkish invasion. Both prediction proved to be correct! Kepler acquired new respect and his salary was increased.

Back to physics and astronomy, while lecturing his mathematics class in Graz, drawing concentric circles and triangles on the blackboard, he suddenly had the epiphany that some figures could fix the ratio between the sizes of two circles, one inscribed and one escribed in and outside of a given triangle. He further realised that by replacing the triangle by a square, then by a regular pentagon, different ratios would emerge. Why could this not explain the relative sizes of the planetary orbits of the Solar System?

Based on ideas of mathematical beauty and symmetry, he suggested that the planetary orbits might be arranged so that regular polygons would just fit between adjacent ones. To Kepler's disappointment, this did not provide the correct ratios. He then had the inspiration that he should be thinking in three spatial dimensions, using spheres rather than circles, tetrahedrons, etc. There were just five regular solids and six planets so it could explain even the number of planets!

Unfortunately, this did not work out either, but Kepler's idea was a good one. Actually, he could have considered how a perturbation to the Solar System would have destroyed agreement, even if it were there at any given time.

Kepler then considered how to explain the fact that the outer planets move more slowly. His first try was as follows:

> "We must choose between two assumptions: either the souls which move the planets are the less active the farther the planet is removed from the sun, or there is only one moving soul in the center of all the orbits, that is the sun, which drives the planet the more vigorously the closer the planet is, but whose force is quasi-exhausted when acting on the outer planets because of the long distance and the weakening of the force which it entails."

Kepler struggled to emerge from medieval concepts that the planets moved because they had souls, i.e. they were alive, magical, and not just lumps of matter. He made a second attempt to answer the same question as follows, years later:

> "If we substitute for the word 'soul' the word 'force' then we get just the principle which underlies my physics of the skies. For once I firmly believed that the motive force of a planet was a soul. Yet as I reflected that this cause of motion diminishes in proportion to distance, just as the light of the sun diminishes in proportion to distance from the sun, I came to the conclusion that this force must be something substantial — 'substantial' not in the literal sense but in the same manner as we say that light is something substantial, meaning by this an unsubstantial entity emanating from a substantial body."

In 1598, Kepler's Graz school closed as were all Lutheran schools by the Archduke Ferdinand of Hapsburg who despised the Lutheran heresy. Kepler stayed for a while, but then had to choose between embracing Catholicism or leaving Austria. He wanted to return to

Tübingen, but that was impossible because of Kepler's embracing Copernicanism.

At this point, Tycho invited Kepler to Prague; Kepler accepted and arrived on January 1, 1600. Kepler quickly realised that in the real world, acquiring Brahe's data would not be easy. Tycho was very secretive and obsessed with his own Tychonic system where the Sun goes around the Earth and all the other planets go around the Sun. Tycho had no motivation to justify the (correct) Copernican system.

In 1601, Tycho's lifestyle caught up with him and he became very ill at a banquet and died of a bladder infection. His heirs were anxious to make money from Tycho's estate. The impoverished Kepler realised that he had to act quickly to get a hold of most of Tycho's data. In a 1605 letter, Kepler wrote the following:

> "I confess that when Tycho died, I quickly took advantage of the absence, or lack of circumspection, of the heirs, by taking the observations under my care, or perhaps usurping them."

Before Kepler even met Tycho, he ventured his opinion in a letter to his mentor Maestlin:

> "My opinion of Tycho is this: he is superlatively rich, but he knows not how to make proper use of it, as is the case with most rich people. Therefore, one must try to wrest his riches from him."

With Tycho's data secured, Kepler decided to use the details to determine the exact orbit of Mars. His preliminary analysis showed that it was close to, but not exactly, a circle and the Sun was not at the centre, but rather up to one tenth of the radius away.

Also Mars's speed varied around its orbit, being fastest at perihelion (nearest the Sun) and slowest at aphelion (furthest away).

Ptolemy had proposed a so-called *equant* model to modify a simple circle, but the new accurate data for the first time could refute the equant theory.

Kepler considered adding epicycles, but believed in a smooth simple orbit. He first improved his knowledge of Earth's orbit since his observations were Earth based. To do this, he used the knowledge of Mars's orbital period of 687.1 days. Tycho had accurate observations going back 25 years so using a Mars–Sun baseline was a brilliant idea.

He found that the Earth's orbit was very close to a circle, varying between 91.4 million miles at perihelion to 94.5 million miles at aphelion, with corresponding speeds 18.2 miles per second and 18.8 miles per second, respectively. He noticed that the speed went inversely as the distance. This can be re-expressed as a radius vector sweeping out equal areas in equal times (Kepler's second Law).

Kepler stared at Mars's orbit as reconstructed from Tycho's data for a *very* long time before he stumbled by chance on the correct answer: it was an ellipse! Kepler said, *I felt as if I had been awakened from a sleep.* This may be why Koestler called his Kepler biography *The Sleepwalkers.* The analysis of Mars's orbit took Kepler 6 years and thousands of pages of calculation.

Kepler had tentative but partially accurate ideas about gravity as noted in his book from 1609 *Astronomia Nova* (New Astronomy):

> "If two stones were placed anywhere in space near to each other, and outside the reach of force of (other bodies), then they would come together at an intermediate point, each approaching the other in proportion to the other's mass."

He also understood that the tides were caused by the waters of the oceans being attracted by the Moon:

> "If the earth ceased to attract the waters of the sea, the seas would rise and flow into the moon."

He went on to add the following:

> "If the attractive force of the moon reaches down to the earth, it follows that the attractive force of the earth, all the more, extends to the moon and even farther."

The obvious question in retrospect is as follows: Why did Kepler not realise that gravity plays a central role in determining the planetary orbits? The answer is almost certainly that he did not understand inertia and believed instead that the planets required a constant force *in the direction of motion* to keep them in their orbits.

He was a mathematics teacher in Graz and an associate of Prince Hans Ulrich von Eggenberg. He was later an assistant to Tycho Brahé in Prague, then Imperial Mathematician to Emperor Rudolf II and to his two successors Matthias and Ferdinand II.

The planetary orbits according to Copernicus obey the following:

(i) The planetary orbit is a circle.
(ii) The Sun is at the centre of the circle.
(iii) The speed of the planet in its orbit is constant.

After the work of Kepler, these rules were modified and generalised to the following:

(i) The planetary orbit is an ellipse.
(ii) The Sun is at one of the two foci of the ellipse.
(iii) The area speed is a constant, as is therefore the angular momentum.

Kepler and Copernicus coincide in the limit of vanishing eccentricity, $\epsilon$. For the Earth, $\epsilon = 0.0167$. Mercury and Mars have the highest eccentricities of all the planets, $\epsilon = 0.2506$ and $\epsilon = 0.0934$, respectively. For Mars, Kepler first found a circle incorrect and had to use an ellipse.

Kepler's Laws of Planetary Motion are as follows:

(1) The orbit of every planet is an ellipse with the Sun at one of the two foci.
(2) A line joining a planet and the Sun sweeps out equal areas during equal intervals of time.
(3) The square of the orbital period of a planet is directly proportional to the square of the semi-major axis of the orbit.

# Chapter 4

# Newton's Gravity

Isaac Newton's *Philosophiae Naturalis Principia Mathematica*, which we can shorten as is usually done to just the *Principia* (1686 for Volume 1, 1687 for Volumes 2 and 3), was written in Latin. The Principia states Newton's laws of motion, forming the foundation of classical mechanics; Newton's law of universal gravitation; and a derivation of Kepler's laws of planetary motion. The Principia is considered one of the most important works in the history of science. The French mathematical physicist Alexis Clairaut assessed it as follows in 1747: "The famous book of *Mathematical Principles of Natural Philosophy* marked the epoch of a great revolution in physics."

Newton was born in 1642 in Woolsthorpe, Lincolnshire, to a middle-class family. He grew to become, during his lifetime, the most famous scientist in the world. In terms of his accomplishments, he is often regarded as the greatest of all physicists and one of the three greatest (with Euler and Gauss) mathematicians.

He was educated at the King's School in Grantham from 1655 to 1660, when he returned to Woolsthorpe and his mother tried to convince Isaac to become a farmer, an occupation which he hated. He returned briefly to the Grantham school and was admitted in 1661 to Trinity College, one of the most prestigious colleges in Cambridge.

At Cambridge, he took the initial steps to invent calculus in 1665, a mathematical theory which would be central to his understanding of motion in classical mechanics. During this undergraduate period, he studied Aristotle, Descartes, and Galileo, as well as Thomas Street (1621–1689), an astronomer from whom he learned of Kepler's laws of planetary motion as discussed in Chapter 3, which played a role in the Principia. He graduated with a BA degree in August 1665, still as a relatively undistinguished student.

During the next 20 months, he changed from undistinguished to very distinguished while Cambridge University was closed by the Great Plague: Newton spent from August 1665 to April 1667 at his home in Woolsthorpe where he made a series of transformative discoveries. This period included the year 1666, often called Newton's *annus mirabilis.*

In 1666, first of all, he completed his formulation of calculus, or *fluxions* as he called it. The idea was mathematically to represent infinitesimal changes in functions resulting from an infinitesimal change of the functional variable. Newton used some notation which we still sometimes use, such as the over-dot, as a shorthand for differentiation.

The calculus was discovered independently by the German mathematician, philosopher, and logician, Gottfried Wilhelm Leibniz (1646–1716). Leibniz used a better notation for his calculus, such as $\frac{dy}{dx}$, and that is what is used today. Calculus led to one of the few priority fights for Newton who was generally secretive about his results and paranoid about others stealing them.

As we shall see, Isaac was not an altogether nice man, although we should perhaps be careful not rush to judgment about somebody with a once-in-a-millennium intellect. In his definitive biography, *Never at Rest* (1980), Richard Westfall wrote in his Preface that even after studying everything about Newton for 20 years he could still not understand what it must have been like to actually be him.

For example, contemporary reports describe Newton as an apparently unhappy man who always looked morose, but perhaps his exceptional creativity was sufficient for him. He never married or had a girlfriend, although there was an unusual relationship with a younger Swiss mathematician, Nicolas Fatio de Dullier (1664–1753), which lasted from 1689 to 1693. Fatio did try to intervene in the Newton–Leibniz controversy, taking the side of Newton, although most scholars believe that their discovery of calculus was independent.

When his relationship with Fatio suddenly ended, it apparently caused Newton to have a mental breakdown (1693). Whether their relationship had a sexual component remains unknown.

A second major discovery in 1666 was that white light can be decomposed into the different colours of the spectrum by passage through a prism, then recombined into white light by a second prism. Newton later pursued many studies in optics, leading to the book *Optiks* (1704).

Returning to Newton's morose appearance, in his decades of research, Westfall found only one example where Newton smiled. It occurred at the High Table in Trinity College, Cambridge, where Newton was a fellow. The President was discussing Euclids's *Elements*, written around 300 BC, and how remarkable it was that mathematicians still studied it 2,000 years after it was written. At this point, another fellow who had Newton in his line of sight noticed Newton smile. It was so unexpected that the other fellow went back to his room and wrote a description of the event, which Westfall found.

The third of the three discoveries made by Newton while at home during 1666 was the law of universal gravitation. This is the greatest discovery ever made by Newton or probably any other physicist and underlies his explanation of the planetary orbits. Newton is thought to have conceived of the gravity idea by seeing an apple fall from its tree in his garden. Some cartoonists have the apple hitting Newton on the head, but that is probably apocryphal. The question was why it fell vertically downward toward the centre of the Earth rather than vertically upward or sideways.

He knew that the Moon orbited the Earth and wondered whether the forces on the apple and the Moon have a common origin. On formulating the inverse square law, he found to his delight that within the accuracy of his calculations, the two forces agreed. All school children with a scientific bent are impressed by the discovery that the weight acting on their feet is the same force as that holding the Moon, often visible at night, in its orbit.

Based on this agreement between the apple and the Moon, Newton stated his law of universal gravitation that "Every particle in the Universe attracts every other particle with a force proportional to the product of their masses and inversely proportional to the square of their distance of separation." The constant of proportionality in the universal law is justifiably called Newton's constant, denoted by $G_N$. Such a maximally broad generalisation from just one example is a sign of Newton's intellect. Remarkably, this law still describes all of gravity from the minimum separation measured, which is a few microns, up to the distance between galaxies, a range of over 20 orders of magnitude.

Some theoretical physicists have proposed modifications of Newton's law to explain, for example, what appears as dark matter when one assumes the law. MOND is an acronym for Modified Newtonian Dynamics. Yet, there is no convincing reason to abandon the law 350 years later, except for the usually small effects of Einstein's general relativity.

When Newton returned to Cambridge in 1667, he was made a fellow of Trinity College. He received a Cambridge MA degree in 1668 and in 1669 was appointed Lucasian Professor at the exceptionally young age of 27. His predecessor, Isaac Barrow (1630–1677), was the first holder of the prestigious chair and recognised Newton's superiority.

Newton had always assumed that the gravitational force obeyed the inverse square law, but his competitor Robert Hooke (1635–1703), a more senior scientist, claimed he had independently had the same idea. This provoked another bitter priority dispute, similar to that with Leibniz, and more intense because Hooke was in England. Later on, after Newton became President of the Royal Society for life (1703–1727), he is said to have personally destroyed an oil painting which had been made of Hooke for the Society. Hooke was short of stature and, when Newton apparently modestly stated in a letter to Hooke that "if I have seen a little further, it is by standing on the shoulders of Giants," some Newton scholars believe he was being sarcastic about Hooke's height. As usual, it is difficult to explain his comments and behaviour.

The way in which Newton was convinced to write the Principia in 1685–1687 is interesting. The one senior physicist whom Newton seems to have trusted was Edmund Halley (1656–1742) whose name is attached to the eponymous comet which has a period of 75–76 years. It last appeared in 1986 and will appear again in mid-2061. It is readily visible to the naked eye with a long tail and it was Halley who accurately predicted its periodicity.

In the summer of 1674, Halley went to ask Newton one question about gravity: what is the orbit of a planet around the Sun, assuming an inverse square law force? Newton immediately answered that it was an ellipse and that he had computed it years ago. When Halley requested the derivation, however, Newton could not find his old notes, but promised to send a copy when he did.

A short time later, Halley received a communication from Newton which revealed how deep the latter's understanding had become, far beyond the knowledge of any other physicist. Halley decided that Newton must be convinced to publish his unique knowledge. This was not easy because of Newton's petulance and paranoia about publishing anything, and he still refused to write a book.

Luckily for posterity, Halley was persistent. He was President of the Royal Society and arranged that the publication costs would be paid by a combination of the Society and from his own pocket. Another guarantee, important to Newton, was that he would have total editorial control and be free to include or exclude anything as he saw fit. In this way, he could include or exclude his big rivals like Leibniz and Hooke as he saw fit.

Finally Halley resorted to flattery, and with access to the monarch, he had King James II write a personal letter to Newton, in which he wrote that his greatest privilege was to be alive at the same time as Isaac. The King also appealed to Newton's patriotism that sharing his knowledge would not only benefit the scientific community but also bring honour to England, and to its monarch. Given the consequences, this may be one of the most important things which James II ever did, although it is barely mentioned in any of his biographies.

This flattery from the monarch apparently did the trick and the very stubborn Newton took on with enthusiasm the huge and challenging task of writing a book which would change western civilisation. The book *Principia* eventually occupied three volumes which took almost 2 years of Newton's effort at Trinity College, Cambridge.

According to contemporaneous accounts, he threw himself into the calculation and writing in an intellectual frenzy. He sometimes neglected to take care of himself, even forgetting to eat and drink properly.

By 1676, he had finished the first volume of the Principia, entitled *De Motu Corporum* (the motion of bodies). It contained his laws of mechanics and his universal gravitation, leading to his explanation of Kepler's Laws. It was written in Latin and with a mastery unprecedented in the physical sciences.

Galileo had begun to study the mechanics of bodies falling or rolling down an inclined plane. Newton made a very perspicuous formulation of the laws of motion from which all of classical mechanics follows. His first law was concerned with inertia, the idea that particles change their motion only under the action of a force. One statement of it is as follows: "A body continues in its state of rest or of motion in a straight line, unless compelled to change that motion by the action of an impressed force." This law of inertia is basic to the whole field of mechanics.

His second law of motion states the following: "The change in momentum of a body is proportional to the magnitude of the impressed force." For a body of a fixed mass, this leads to the famous equation $F = ma$ or force equals mass times acceleration. From this, the properties of motions with uniform acceleration result.

School children learn about Newton's mechanics just as they learn about Euclid's geometry. They use it to calculate the motion of falling bodies, of weights hanging from systems of pulleys, and the parabolic trajectories of objects in a uniform gravitational field. Usually, the first step is to draw a force diagram which indicates all the forces acting on the system. Here, forces resulting from a third law must all be included.

Newton's third and last law is as follows: "Action and reaction are equal and opposite." This means, for example, that the Earth pushes vertically upward, equally and oppositely to the weight vertically downward so that there is no net motion. A complete diagram of the forces acting on any system must include such reaction forces in order to correctly calculate the resultant motion.

These three Netwton's Laws of Motion reduce to a bare minimum the basic axioms of classical mechanics. During the next two centuries, two leading mathematicians provided elegant reformulations of Newtonian mechanics. The first was the Italian Joseph-Louis Lagrange (1736–1813) who succeeded Leonhard Euler (1707–1783) as the head of the Prussian Academy in 1766. The second was the Irish mathematician William Rowland Hamilton (1805–1865) who also discovered quaternions.

These so-called Lagrangian and Hamiltonian versions of classical mechanics provide powerful frameworks for calculation. The Lagrangian is especially widely used in classical, and quantum, field theory. However, both are strictly equivalent to Newton's version, provided in the first volume *De Motu Corporum* of the *Principia.* Nothing fundamentally different from the Principia on classical mechanics appeared until the special relativity of Einstein (1905) over 200 years later. Twenty years after Einstein, Heisenberg (1925) discovered quantum mechanics, which also corrects Newtonian mechanics at atomic distances.

Also in Volume 1 of *Principia* was the law of universal gravitation and its application to motion in a gravitational field. Newton realised that, if there existed a 5-mile-high mountain on the Earth with a gun at the top, shooting a shell horizontally with sufficient velocity would make it go entirely around the Earth and return to the starting point. The necessary speed for this, now called the orbital velocity, is about 25,000 m.p.h. In a related calculation, the necessary speed vertically upward to become free from the Earth's gravitational pull, now called the escape velocity, is about 18,000 m.p.h.

He applied his law of universal gravitation to the planets and could readily derive all three of Kepler's Laws. The orbits must be ellipses with the Sun at one of the two foci, thus the first law.

Conservation of angular momentum required a radius vector between the Sun and a planet to sweep out equal area in equal times, which is the second Kepler law.

These two laws apply separately to each planet. The third law relates different planets and relates the orbital periods to the planetary distances from the Sun. Its derivation by Newton required precisely an inverse square dependence for the gravitational force. No other distance dependence would lead to the third law.

All of this was in the first volume and it showed the world how the workings of the universe follow mathematical laws and provided a venerable origin to the field of theoretical physics.

The second volume of *Principia*, published in 1687, ventured into fluid dynamics including Newton's brilliant but wrong calculation of the speed of sound in air. At the time, there were measurements of this speed at 20°C and one atmospheric pressure (76 cm of mercury), giving an average value of about 343 m/s.

Newton made an inspired guess for the dependence on pressure and density but, to his consternation, his theory gave a value of about 298 m/s, some 15% too low. Determined to arrive at the correct answer, he invented two imaginative corrections.

The first he called *crassitude*, by which he meant that he had neglected the finite size of the air molecules which he somehow argued would increase the sound speed by the infinite sound speed across the molecules. By this false argument, he could find a 10% increase, still not enough to agree with experiment.

He therefore invented a second correction. Here, he came up with the most ridiculous item in the whole *Principia.* He decided that air contained foreign vapours which somehow altered the speed of sound. In private correspondence, Newton confided that he thought the foreign vapours must come from France! In any case, the combination of crassitude and foreign vapours could, according to Newton, provide excellent agreement between theory and experiment.

The truth of the matter is that sound propagates in a different way from how Newton imagined it. It is not at constant temperature (isothermal), but at constant entropy (adiabatic) because there is insufficient time for the temperature to readjust. The concept of entropy was not introduced until 1865 and if the sound speed is calculated correctly, adiabatically, a correction factor near 1.15 appears and provides the correct answer.

For Newton to achieve the correct answer, he would have had to realise not only entropy but the fact that air molecules are diatomic. What seems interesting to us about this vignette is the infinite self-belief he possessed and demonstrated by being so certain he could fudge his sound speed result.

Incidentally, who measured the speed of sound? It was Newton himself who measured it in Trinity College, Cambridge, in Neville's Court by striking a rock with a hammer and timing the delay until the echo from the other side of the quad sounded. In this way, he obtained a good value for the speed of sound. He was a triple threat, as a theoretical physicist, experimental physicist, and mathematician.

As an experimentalist, Newton also showed his worth by measurements in optics. Using lenses and prisms, he overcame the prevailing idea that pure light was fundamentally white and colourless. Newton counted seven colours in the spectrum: red, orange, yellow, green, blue, indigo, and violet. In his second most important book *Opticks*, "A Treatise of the Reflexions, Refractions, Inflexions and Colours of Light (1704)," he gave an impressive account of his optical studies.

This second book shares some of the importance of the *Principia*, and records experiments and deductions made from them. It covers phenomena of diffraction, which Newton called inflexion.

In particular, it discusses the dispersion or separation of light into its spectrum of component colours. It shows that colour appears, arising from selective absorption, reflection, or transmission of the different components.

The ancient Greeks, Aristotle and Theophrastus (371 BC–287 BC), had asserted the dogma believed widely for more than a millennium that light from the Sun is white and becomes coloured only due to mixture with darkness due to interactions with matter. Newton's *Opticks* proved that the opposite is true and that light is composed of all the different colours.

The different colours are deflected by different angles through a prism and can be recombined by a second prism. He argued that colour is a sensation within the mind and not an inherent property of materials or light.

Many of Newton's ideas became central to the design of tunable lasers in the 20th century and to the evolution of multi-prism dispersion theory.

The 1704 book, unlike *Principia* in the 1680s, was written in English rather than Latin. Also, it does not proceed by propositions, lemmas, and axioms, but rather everything stems from carefully described experiments. Having said that, *Opticks* does develop conjectures about light that go beyond the experimental evidence.

Newton favoured the *corpuscular* nature of light where it is composed of small particles, and the perceived colours were harmonically proportioned like a musical scale.

At the end of *Opticks*, there is a series of *Queries* allowing Newton to pontificate on a wide range of physics issues including not only optics but also heat, gravity, electricity, and chemical reactions. Even the ethical behaviour of human beings was included. There were 16 queries in the first edition, which became more than 30 in the fourth edition. One of the most famous is his 31st query, which anticipates much later developments in chemical affinity.

One passage in the Queries section of *Opticks* reads as follows:

> "And since Space is divisible in infinitum, and Matter is not necessarily in all places, it may be also allow'd that God is able to create Particles of Matter of several Sizes and Figures, and in several Proportions to Space, and perhaps of different Densities and Forces, and thereby to vary the Laws of Nature, and make Worlds of several sorts in several Parts of the Universe. At least, I see nothing of Contradiction in all this."

This can be interpreted as an anticipation of the *multiverse* which became popular in superstring theory in the later 20th century.

It is interesting that Newton delayed publication of Opicks until the year after Robert Hooke died in 1703. Hooke had disputed the corpuscular theory of light. The reception of both *Principia* and *Opticks* by some intellectuals in France was initially negative because of the dramatic departure from the ancient Greeks. Newton pushed the use of mathematical reasoning to experience or experiment.

Voltaire (1694–1778) (*nom de plume* of Francois-Marie Arouet) did much to publicise and popularise these works in *Elements de la philosophie de Newton* (1738) and by 1750, Newtonian science was firmly established almost everywhere.

Of course, later physicists amended Newton's concepts in the *Opticks.* In particular, Christiaan Huygens (1629–1695) and Thomas Young (1773–1829) formulated the wave theory of light and identified colours with different wavelengths.

Newton also built the first reflecting telescope.

As a mathematician, he contributed to the study of power series, generalised the binomial theorem to non-integer powers, evolved a method to approximate the roots of a function, and classified many of the cubic plane curves.

Newton can be readily classified as the best of all time in Physics *and* simultaneously the third best in Mathematics (after Gauss and Euler).

Apart from all his broad and brilliant scientific work, he acted briefly as a Member of Parliament in 1689–1690 and 1701–1702. However, his only comments were to complain about draughts in the chamber and requests that the window be closed. He was ineffective in enacting any new laws.

Newton was appointed Warden (1696–1700) then Master (1700–1727) of the Royal Mint. For most appointees, these jobs were regarded as mere sinecures, but he took a keen interest in counterfeiters who could be sentenced to death when convicted. Counterfeiting was a high treason felony punishable by being hanged, drawn and quartered. He invented the idea of milling around the edge of coins to make copying them more difficult.

Newton always attended the hangings of convicted forgers and took a great interest in it even to the point of pulling the execution lever. This suggests an unusually sadistic bent.

Why is Newton such a legendary genius? Surely, it rests mostly on his law of universal gravitation, which he discovered at the age of

24 at home during the Great Plague. This was such a revolutionary discovery that it changed everything.

Then, there is the *Principia*, finally published in 1687 and dedicated naturally to King James II of England. This book was read by the great scientists of Europe and, although there was initial skepticism, it had such a lasting impact that academicians became shocked by the surpassing quality of Newton's work.

The book presented a towering shadow over science and advanced physics by 150–200 years single-handedly. It is true that it is not read 2,000 years later like Euclid's *Elements*, but this depends on the nature of the subjects of mathematics and physics where results in the former remain permanent and those of the latter constantly progress.

As active particle theorists in the 2020s, neither of the authors need to read the *Principia* as it is obsolete and superseded. Nevertheless, we must acknowledge that, had Newton never existed, physics could now be decades or centuries behind its present level.

This is purely hypothetical and we should better follow Newton's own dictum in *Principia* when he wrote *Hypotheses non fingo*, meaning "I do not make hypotheses". What Newton meant in that context was that he did not want to speculate about the cause of gravity, only to state that it existed and obeyed, for an unknown reason, a very-well-defined mathematical law.

Newton (1642 to 1726–1727) was knighted by Queen Anne in 1705 and so, given that he was already lifetime President of the Royal Society, he could, if he wished, write his own name *Sir Isaac Newton, PRS.*

A century after Newton's universal gravitation, in 1766, John Dalton was born into a Quaker family (we saw that the Quaker group belongs to the evolutionist group) in Eaglesfield, near Cockermouth, in Cumberland, England. Dalton resigned the position at the "New College" in Manchester at age 34, i.e. in 1800 because of the college's worsening financial situation at that time and began a new career as a private tutor in mathematics and natural philosophy. He was a chemist, physicist, and meteorologist. He proposed the atomic theory in 1803 that each chemical element is composed of atoms of a single, unique type, and though they cannot be altered or destroyed by chemical means, they can combine to form more complex structures (chemical compounds). Since Dalton reached his conclusions by experimentation and examination of the results in an empirical fashion, this marked the first truly scientific theory of the atom.

He enunciated Gay-Lussac's law, published in 1802 by Joseph Louis Gay-Lussac (Gay-Lussac credited the discovery to unpublished work from the 1780s by Jacques Charles). In the 2 or 3 years following the lectures, Dalton published several papers on similar topics. *On the Absorption of Gases by Water and other Liquids* (read as a lecture on October 21, 1803, first published in 1805)[1] contained his law of partial pressures now known as Dalton's law. In it, he said the following:

> "Why does not water admit its bulk of every kind of gas alike? This question I have duly considered, and though I am not able to satisfy myself completely I am nearly persuaded that the circumstance depends on the weight and number of the ultimate particles of the several gases."

By studying Dalton's laboratory notebooks, discovered in the rooms of the Manchester Literary and Philosophical Society, Roscoe and Harden stated in 1897[2] that the idea of atoms arose in Dalton's mind as a purely physical concept, forced on him by study of the physical properties of the atmosphere and other gases.

Dalton's atomic theory opened a new chapter in chemistry.

---

[1] J. Dalton, "III. On the absorption of gases by water and other liquids", *The Philosophical Magazine*, **24**(93), 15–24 (1806).

[2] H. E. Roscoe and A. Harden, *A New View of the Origin of Dalton's Atomic Theory* (Macmillan, London, 1896), ISBN 978-1-4369-2630-0.

## Chapter 5

# Darwinian Evolution

Let us begin the post-Enlightenment era with the giant gap between the first atomist, Democritus, and the modern atomist, Mendeleev.

Dmitri Ivanovich Mendeleev (08.02.1834–02.02.1907) was a Russian chemist and inventor. He is best known for periodic table in his name. Russian physicist Andrei Matlashov informs that Mendeleev was born in the village of Verkhnie Aremzyani, near Tobolsk in Siberia, to Ivan Pavlovich Mendeleev (1783–1847) and Maria Dmitrievna Mendeleeva (née Kornilieva) (1793–1850). Ivan worked as a school principal and a teacher of fine arts, politics and philosophy at the Tambov and Saratov gymnasiums. Dmitri's grandfather, Pavel Maximovich Sokolov, was a Russian Orthodox priest from the Tver region.

Mendeleev was raised as an Orthodox Christian, his mother encouraging him to "patiently search divine and scientific truth", but Mendeleev seemed to have very few theological commitments. Mendeleev's son Ivan said, "...from his earliest years Father practically split from the church–and if he tolerated certain simple everyday rites, then only as an innocent national tradition, similar to Easter cakes, which he didn't consider worth fighting against.... Mendeleev's opposition to traditional Orthodoxy was not due to either atheism or a scientific materialism".[1] Rather, he held to a form of romanticised deism about God not involving Himself in human

[1]Michael D. Gordin, *A Well-ordered Thing: Dmitrii Mendeleev and the Shadow of the Periodic Table* (Basic Books, 2004), pp. 229–230; ISBN 978-0-465-02775-0.

affairs even if He created the world. At age 21 in 1855, he moved to the Crimean Peninsula on the northern coast of the Black Sea in order to cure his tuberculosis. In 1857, he returned to S. Petersburg with fully restored health. He got a tenure at St. Petersburg University in 1867 and started to teach inorganic chemistry.

During 1868 and 1870, Mendeleev wrote the two-volume textbook, *Fundamentals of Chemistry.* After finishing the first part at the end of 1868, he was on a two-week business travel from February 17, 1869, looking for dairy farms. He was under the extreme Zeitnöt (time pressure) with the desire to finish the table needed for the next lectures from March 1, 1869, at St. Petersburg University and to fulfil the business duty, but this was the time when he made his most important table. At this time, he had the basic idea of making a table by placing chemical elements along the atomic weights like arranging cards by the suits, and the first part dealt with alkali metals and haploids. He remembered all 63 elements by heart and placed 43 on the table and 20 on the margin, trying to put them into the table. On February 17, 1869, he placed all 63 elements on the table without any element in the margin, as shown in Fig. 1. But, question marks appear on Table 1.

Another person classifying chemical elements in the early 1860s was Lothar Meyer who listed 28 elements classified by their valence, but not with atomic weights. Mendeleev was unaware of Meyer's work going on in the 1860s.[2] As he attempted to classify the elements according to their chemical properties, by atomic weights, he noticed patterns that finally led him to postulate his periodic table. According to his friend, Inostrantzev, he claimed to have envisioned the complete arrangement of the elements in a dream, "I saw in a dream a table where all elements fell into place as required. Awakening, I immediately wrote it down on a piece of paper, only in one place did a correction later seem necessary," as quoted by

[2]B. M. Kedrov, On the Question of the Psychology of Scientific Creativity (On the Occasion of the Discovery by D. I. Mendeleev of the Periodic Law), *A Journal of Translations*, **VIII**(2), 18–37 (1967), translated by H. A. Simon (Carnegie Institute of Technology) from [Voprosy psikhologii, **3**(6), 91–113 (1957)].

Figure 1: Mendeleev's handwriting taken from Karpov's talk.

Kedrov on the occasion of the fiftieth anniversary of the death of Mendeleev. By adding additional elements following this pattern, Mendeleev placed them in a "periodic" way and arranged them according to their atomic mass, as shown in Fig. 1,[3] so that groups of elements with similar properties fell into horizontal columns (now, chemical "groups" are shown vertically in contrast to their horizontal format in Mendeleev's table). Mendeleev's version had period 8 for 63 elements.

On March 6, 1869, he made a formal presentation of this table to the Russian Chemical Society, titled *The Dependence between the Properties of the Atomic Weights of the Elements*, which described elements according to both valence and atomic weight. The number

[3]A. Karpov, Synthesis of superheavy elements: Present and future, Talk presented at the *19th Lomonosov Conference on Elementary Particle Physics*, Moscow State University, August 22–28, 2019.

Table 1: Mendeleev's *Tentative System of Elements* (63 elements) written on February 17, 1869 as Fig. 1.

| | | | Ti = 50 | Zr = 90 | ? = 180 |
|---|---|---|---|---|---|
| | | | V = 51 | Nb = 94 | Ta = 182. |
| | | | Cr = 52 | Mo = 96 | W = 186. |
| | | | Mn = 55 | Rh = 104.4 | Pt = 197.4 |
| | | | Fe = 56 | Rn = 104.4 | Ir = 198 |
| | | | Ni = 59 | Pl = 106.6 | Cs = 199 |
| H = 1 | ? = 8 | ? = 22 | Cu = 63.4 | Ag = 108 | Hg = 200 |
| | Be = 9.4 | Mg = 24 | Zn = 65.2 | Cd = 112 | |
| | B = 11 | Al = 27.4 | ? = 68 | Ur = 116 | Au = 197.? |
| | C = 12 | Si = 28 | ? = 70 | Sn = 118 | |
| | N = 14 | P = 31 | As = 75 | Sb = 122 | Bi = 210.? |
| | O = 16 | S = 32 | Se = 79.4 | Te = 128? | |
| | F = 19 | Cl = 35.5 | Br = 80 | I = 127 | |
| Li = 7 | Na = 23 | K = 39 | Rb = 85.4 | Cs = 133 | Tl = 204 |
| | | Ca = 40 | Sr = 87.6 | Ba = 137 | Pb = 207. |
| | | ? = 45 | Ce = 92 | | |
| | | ? Er = 56? | La = 94 | | |
| | | ? Yt = 60 | Di = 95 | | |
| | | ?In = 78.6?? | Th = 118? | | |

of natural elements are 92 with uranium being the 92nd. Now, artificial elements with valence exceeding 92 are manufactured and so far Atomic Number 115 has been observed. Hints of Nature to atomists have been revealed first by the regularity as Mendeleev noticed and later by Murray Gell-Mann in his 1960s eight-fold way of hadrons.

When Mendeleev told the story of his dream to Inostrantzev, he was quoted to have said "after three sleepless nights", but from many sources, the writing of Fig. 1 was a single-day event on February 17, 1869 under the extreme Zeitnöt.

On the back of the letter for the day's official program, Mendeleev wrote, during the breakfast time, his first calculations upon comparing the group of alkaline metals and other groups. This might have been based on his dream of the previous night. His coffee mug was on the paper and left a "trifle" mark on the letter. Historians should pay attention to such "trifles" to convince people that the discovery was a single-day event, as mentioned by Kerdrov. But, this story was in echo (in another aspect) with the second author's frequent teachings to the university students to prepare enough for the exciting moment similar to a lion that frequently sharpens his teeth for the next hunt. Without preparation, he would not get profit from such jolting moments. The exact person in question Mendeleev, had no illusions. What he needed was just the jolt of February 17, 1869.

Mendeleev was a preservationist of Earth, as he remarked that burning petroleum as a fuel "would be akin to firing up a kitchen stove with bank notes",[4] and hence a true atomist. It is known that he was against the scientific claims of spiritualism. He bemoaned the generally accepted spiritualism in Russia and its negative effects on the study of science.

In the 19th century, thermodynamics played a major role in the evolution of theoretical physics, leading to the profound and slightly mysterious concept of entropy. The French physicist who was the father of thermodynamics and whose work started the intellectual path towards entropy was Sadi Carnot (1796–1832). In an 1824 book, Carnot began a new field of research, thermodynamics, and his Carnot Cycle was what later led the German physicist Clausius to the idea of entropy in 1865. The Carnot Cycle is a simple model which mimics the operation of a steam engine.

Rudolf Clausius (1822–1888), a German physicist and mathematician, may justly be regarded as the father of entropy. He was initially inspired by the Carnot Cycle which requires the equality of a ratio of heat energy to absolute temperature for the hot and cold heat reservoirs.

In the presence of irreversible processes in a variant of the Carnot Cycle, one would, instead of this equality, arrive at an inequality which gives rise to the second law of thermodynamics that entropy denoted $S$ (closely related to the ratio (heat)/(temperature)) cannot

[4]J. W. Moore; C. L. Stanitski and P. C. Jurs, *Chemistry: The Molecular Science*, Volume 1 (Brooks/Cole, 2014); ISBN-13: 978-1285199047.

decrease. This led Clausius to a definition for incremental entropy as the exact differential near to thermal equilibrium and thence to the second law of thermodynamics $dS \geq 0$. We emphasise that Clausius's discussion is appropriate only near to thermal equilibrium because a thermally insulated box of ideal gas with an unlikely initial condition, e.g. all the molecules in one corner, will rapidly increase its entropy to approach thermal equilibrium despite the fact that $\delta Q \equiv 0$. Clausius denoted entropy by $S$ in honour of **S**adi Carnot.

Clausius enunciated two laws of thermodynamics as follows:

1. The energy of the universe is a constant.
2. The entropy of the universe tends to a maximum.

Kinetic theory shows how the $P, V, T$ thermodynamic variables can be related to the average motions of the molecules using statistical mechanics. The question following Clausius's work was how to relate the state function $S$ to microscopic variables. Ludwig Boltzmann (1844–1906) was the physicist who solved this problem. He had no experimental evidence for molecules; this had to wait 30 more years until the explanation of Brownian motion in 1905 by Einstein and Smoluchowski.

Regarding Boltzmann, few people were convinced of the reality of atoms and molecules before the last year of his life. Further, his statistical, hence inexact, second law of thermodynamics was strongly criticised by Maxwell who, although he believed in atoms and molecules, never accepted Boltzmann's 1872 idea of an inexact law of physics. Boltzmann appreciated that his law was so unlikely to be violated that it might as well have been exact.

Another severe criticism came from the distinguished French mathematician Henri Poincaré (1854–1912) who proved a rigorous recurrence theorem which states that all systems must return eventually to their original state. Boltzmann understood that the timescale involved in Poincaré recurrence is far too long to be physically relevant. In any case, Boltzmann's lack of recognition in the physics and mathematics communities may have contributed to his suicide at the early age of 62 in 1906.

Boltzmann defined as *microstates* all the possible arrangements of microscopic variables corresponding to a given fixed set of macroscopic or thermodynamic variables whereupon he defined $S = k \ln W$, where $W$ is the total number of microstates. This is one of the most celebrated equations in all of physics and is written as an epitaph on Boltzmann's tomb in Vienna Central Cemetery.

For an ideal gas, the maximisation of entropy $S$ means that in the state of thermal equilibrium, there is the maximum uncertainty in the molecular motions. We can equivalently say that there is the greatest disorder in thermal equilibrium and hence this entropy is a measure of disorder when disorder is suitably defined.

The H theorem of Boltzmann in 1872 is central to physics although even now in 2019 we are told that it cannot be rigorously proved mathematically because, at least far away from equilibrium, it is unknown whether solutions of the Boltzmann transport equation have sufficient analytic smoothness. Nevertheless, the H theorem shows how starting from reversible microscopic mechanics, one can arrive at non-reversible, in a statistical sense, macroscopic dynamics. It explicates the second law of thermodynamics that the entropy of an isolated system cannot decrease. As we deviate from thermal equilibrium, however, the second law must be generalised by the use of the so-called fluctuation theorem.

The paper by Boltzmann in which he proved the H theorem has been studied and criticised probably as much as any physics paper. One interesting critique is by Von Neumann (1903–1957).

The reason why the H theorem of Boltzmann is far more powerful than the infinitesimal definition of $dS$ by Clausius is that it proves that $dS \geq 0$ for non-equilibrium systems assuming only the Boltzmann transport equation, the ergodic hypothesis and *Stosszhalansatz* which is German for molecular chaos that neglects correlations.

What is clear about $S(t)$ for a box of ideal gas is that with thermal equilibrium $S(t)$ is a maximum. From the definition of $S$, this implies that the number of microstates corresponding to the thermally equilibrated system is the highest and that the molecular motion is therefore the most disordered.

Figure 2: John Ellis wrote the SM equations on a CERN mug.

The H theorem encapsulates this edifice of 19th-century knowledge sufficiently to progress with some confidence from a box of ideal gas to more interesting cases such as the early universe, where the concept of the entropy of the universe may be useful.

Some 300 miles north from Kiderminster, James Maxwell (1831–1879) was born in Edinburgh, Scotland. His contribution in kinetic theory of gases is paramount but his equations of 1861, *On Physical Lines of Forces*,[5] unifying electricity and magnetism, outstand it. In the subsequent paper of 1865, *A Dynamical Theory of the Electromagnetic Fields*,[6] we can count eight equations that we use today. In the modern agreement, one equation, the first line on a CERN mug shown in Fig. 2, is enough and even contains more. The only other correct equations known before World War II and still used by modern atomic theorists are Einstein's gravitational equation, not shown in the mug, and Dirac's equation shown in the second and third lines for quarks and leptons.

[5] J. C. Maxwell, On Physical Lines of Forces, *Philosophical Magazine & Journal of Science*, **March** (1861).

[6] J. C. Maxwell, A Dynamical Theory of the Electromagnetic Fields, *Philosophical Transactions of the Royal Society of London* **155**, 459–512 (1865).

Breaking of the 20th century opened the gate to a long tunnel leading to the modern day atomic theory. In 1896, Henri Becquerel (1852–1908) noticed $\beta$-spectrum from the radioactive nuclei, which is a beam of the fundamental particle electron. A year later, John Thompson (1856–1940) showed that cathode rays were composed of previously unknown negatively charged particles which he calculated must have bodies much smaller than atoms and a very large charge-to-mass ratio. Now, Thompson is credited for the discovery of electron while Becquerel is credited for observing the weak interaction phenomena for the first time. From the study of blackbody spectrum, it was necessary to introduce the quantum idea of Max Planck (1858–1947) with a new fundamental constant of Nature with his name attached, $h$. When any physics calculation involves $h$, it is a quantum phenomena. This constant being so important, modern atomists mostly researching quantum phenomena agreed not to write $h$ explicitly. Now, Planck rests at the Göttingen Cemetery with Max Born and several other German Nobel laureates. In this breaking period, a particle introduced with $h$ for the first time was by Albert Einstein (1879–1955) on the nature of already known Maxwell's electromagnetic wave. In the visible light range, it is called "photon" ("-on" means a particle physicist's favourite naming system for a fundamental particle), which (not the relativity theory) awarded him the Nobel prize.

Steven Weinberg[7] classifies the giant physicists into *sages* and *magicians*: "sage-physicists reason in an orderly way about physical problems on the basis of fundamental ideas of the way that nature ought to be ... magician-physicists who do not seem to reason at all but jump over all intermediate steps to new insights about nature." Early quantum theorists and the modern atomists are mostly magicians. Albert Einstein and Wolfgang Pauli are considered to be sages and Werner Heisenberg, Erwin Schrödinger, and Niels Bohr are considered to be magicians. In proposing particles, both

[7]S. Weinberg, *Dreams of a Final Theory* (Vintage Books, Random House, New York, 1994).

Einstein and Pauli worked like magicians for photon in 1905 and for neutrino in 1930, respectively.

Formulation of quantum mechanics in the mid-1920s was a revolution in atomic physics, even more so than Newton's classical mechanics. Quantum mechanics provided the notion of identical particles that was one of the postulates of the Greek atomists. A brief history until 1926 is as follows. After Niels Bohr declared the allowed atomic orbits in 1913, it was the problem of physicists to understand the energy levels of the Bohr atom. It occurred to Werner Heisenberg in 1925 during his escape to Heligoland Island in North Sea that Bohr's atomic orbit is not observable and hence one can consider a scheme with only measurable numbers, a thread leading to his great achievement. The final outcome of his study with only measurable numbers such as position and momentum is now known as matrix mechanics, which is one version of quantum mechanics. There is another formulation called wave mechanics, known as Schrödinger's work, which have become the working ground of theoretical chemistry. The idea is based on the wave function. For any observable, there exists the wave function denoted as $\Psi$.

The wave function idea was first introduced by a French physicist, Louis Victor Pierre Raymond de Broglie, 7th duc de Broglie, in 1923. He postulated the wave nature of electrons, giving the electron wavelength proportional to the inverse of its momentum and suggested that all matter has wave properties. There is an anecdote on how Schrödinger is related to the wave function. In 1921, Schrödinger at age 32 moved to the ETH Zürich, where the leader was 37 year old Peter Debye (1916–2012). In 1925, de Broglie gave a seminar on his electron wave at ETH. After the seminar, Debye asked de Broglie, "I know that all waves have the wave equations that they follow. If yours is matter wave, what is your equation of motion?" when de Broglie could not answer the question, Debye turned to Schrödinger and told him,[8] "Rather than going out for hiking, get the equation of de Broglie's." In 1926, Schrödinger happily obtained

[8]Susumu Okubo's comment to the second author at Rochester, New York, January, 2010.

his equation for matter waves, which included a phase $i$ unlike in all other previous wave equations.

The interpretation of the wave function based on the work of the German mathematician at Göttingen, Max Born (1882–1970), is that it is the probability amplitude, i.e. the probability to find a matter particle is proportional to $|\Psi|^2$. Göttingen, the centre of the Germany map, was the centre of new physics in 1920s. Heisenberg, Dirac, and Oppenheimer came to Göttingen and were guided by Max Born, whose tombstone at the Göttingen Cemetery reads $pq - qp = \frac{h}{2\pi i}$, where $h$ is the Planck constant. This is Heisenberg's uncertainty relation and it seems that the Göttingen group considered it as their work. The probability interpretation invites transformations which do not change the probability, i.e. the electron number is not created or destroyed. If we multiply a phase to the wave function, $e^{i\alpha}\Psi$, the probability $|\Psi|^2$ remains the same. Thus, in quantum mechanics, we consider only the probability conserving transformations. A generalisation of $e^{i\alpha}$ is the unitary transformation $e^{i\alpha_i F^i}$, where $F_i$ is called the generators of the unitary transformation. In this regard, Chen Ning Yang called quantum mechanics *phase mechanics.*

Heisenberg introduced the notion of *uncertainty principle.* In mathematics, any well-behaved function in a definite region can be written as a linear sum of functions of a complete set in the defined region. For example, for $x$ in the region $x \in [0, 2\pi)$, $\sin x$ can be written as a Taylor series: $\sin x = x - \frac{x^3}{3!} + \frac{x^5}{5!} + \cdots$ since $\{1, x, x^2, \ldots\}$ is a complete set. If $x$ denotes the coordinate of the measurable displacement, any wave function can be a function of $x$ only, $\Psi(x)$. But, the linear momentum in classical mechanics of a particle at $x$ is $p = \frac{dx}{dt}$. To relate to this classical relation, it is noted that $\frac{dx}{dt}$ is related to $x$ but not as a function of $x$ only. It involves the derivative with respect to $t$. For an $x$-dependent function $\Psi(x)$, the $t$ dependence can be only by the derivative $\frac{d\Psi(x)}{dt}$ for $\Psi(x)$ now a function of $t$ through $x(t)$. So, we consider only differentiable functions for $\Psi(x(t))$. Differential operation acts on the function $\Psi(x(t))$. With this definable setup, we can calculate $p\Psi(x(t))$. But, in the operation $p(x\Psi(x))$, $p$ with the act of differentiation just does not go through $x$. Therefore, $(xp - px)\Psi(x) = \Psi(x)$, introducing a non-vanishing commutator for $x$ and $p$. $(xp - px)$ is denoted as the commutator $[x, p]$ written on the tombstone of Max Born.

One complete set of functions in the interval $x = (-\pi, +\pi]$ is $\{e^{inx}, n = \text{integer}\}$ in terms of which we can expand any differentiable function $\Psi(x)$, which is called Fourier series. This can be generalised to a continuous variable, $n \to k$ (or $p$), which is called "Fourier transformation". As commented before, this transformation using $e^{ikx}$ is the probability conserving transformation. Explicitly, the Fourier transformation is $\Psi'(p) \propto \int dx\, e^{ixp/\hbar}\Psi(x)$ where $\hbar$ has the dimension of $[\text{cm} \cdot \frac{\text{gram cm}}{\text{s}}] = [\text{energy} \cdot \text{time}]$. Because the wave function involves two measurable variables $x$ and $p$ with the locked-up phase $e^{ixp/\hbar}$, they have the uncertainty relation $[x, p] = i\hbar$, where $\hbar \equiv h/2\pi$. If two observables do not have that locked-up phase, they do not have the uncertainty relation. In most undergraduate textbooks on quantum mechanics, therefore, the uncertainty relation is exercised in terms of Fourier transformation.

On the right-hand side of the uncertainty relation, the so-called Planck constant $\hbar$ describes how visible is the quantum effects are. The action unit is represented in units of the Planck constant $\hbar$.[9] If the action is order 1 compared to the Planck constant $\hbar$, then the quantum effect is manifest. If the action is much larger than 1 compared to the Planck constant $\hbar$, then the quantum effect oscillates out. Since the Planck constant $\hbar$ has the unit [energy $\cdot$ time], (time) $\times$ (energy) can appear in the phase in the unitary transformation $\Psi'(p) \propto \int dx\, e^{-itE/\hbar}\Psi(x)$. Therefore, the energy–momentum relation of observables $E$ and $p$ in classical mechanics, $E = \frac{p^2}{2m} + V(x)$, written on wave function introduces $i$ on the left-hand side of the Schrödinger equation. The relativistic generalisation of the Schrödinger equation is the Klein–Gordon equation for spin-0 waves and the Dirac equation for spin-$\frac{1}{2}$ waves.

One crucial part missed by the earlier atomists (Democritus, Epicurus, Lucretius, Dalton, Mendeleev, Bohr) is the concept of rotation of indivisible atoms or particles. Atoms could not be seen

[9] There is another number under the name of Planck mass: $M_P = 2.43 \times 10^{18}$ GeV.

with the traditional light microscopes invented in the 17th century. As mentioned in Chapter 1, Robert Hooke observed the "teeth of time" in 1655 with the light microscope. The scanning tunnelling microscopes of today, imaging surfaces at the atomic level, cannot see the rotation either. From time to time these days, we watch in the TV news the current nanotechnology achievements, showing images of the sizes larger than a 10-millionth cm, roughly 10 times larger than the sizes of atoms. Even popular physics books written these days[10] do not emphasise the importance of rotation of elementary particles mainly because the "V–A" quartet had not been credited by the Nobel Committee. Now, the Committee lost its chance since all the four (Feynman, Gell-Mann, Marshak, and Sudarshan), involved in the initial discovery of interactions related to the rotation of fundamental particles, passed away. In the beginning of Chapter 8, we discuss more about their ideas.

Rotations of Sun, Moon, and Planets in their orbits were known to Greeks, but the concept of rotation was not used in their atomic theory. Even if the idea were used then, this kind of orbit could not be successfully embedded in their atomic theory. Figure 3(a) shows an orbital rotation for one cycle. If one looks at it, it is rotating in the counterclockwise direction from top and clockwise direction from bottom. Therefore, clockwise or counterclockwise rotations of an orbital rotation of a star in the heaven are not distinguished. But, if a top is rotating, then one can say whether it is rotating clockwise or counterclockwise; see Fig. 4 showing as Wolfgang Pauli and Niels Bohr watch a rotating top. In fact, the rotation of the top is an orbital rotation because each point in the top rotates along its orbit of rotation. The clockwise or counterclockwise sense of Pauli and Bohr was because they could not see the rotation from under the floor.

If rotation of an electron around nucleus, which Niels Bohr modelled for the Hydrogen energy spectrum, is considered, then again the rotational orbit is the first guess. But, if the size of something

---

[10] B. Green, *The Elegant Universe* (W. W. Norton, USA, 2003) and C. Rovelli, *Reality is Not What it Seems* (in English) (Penguin Group, New York, 2016).

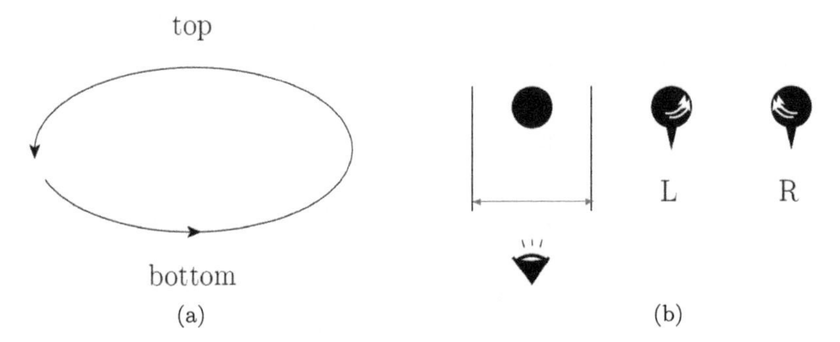


Figure 3: Rotations: (a) rotation along an orbit; (b) consideration for possible rotations of an atom, and L and R from the top view.

Figure 4: Wolfgang Pauli, the inventor of word "spin", and Niels Bohr, the inventor of his atomic model, watching a spinning top.

is very small for our ability (the range of red arrows) of measuring its size, as shown on the left-hand side in Fig. 3(b), the story is different. In this case, there is no way to convince ourselves about the clockwise or counterclockwise sense of rotation of the object. The size of an object must be covered in the atomic theory.

Peeling the onion structure of matter, we end up with the indivisible atoms. In fact, Democritus's atom must be interpreted as being smaller than Bohr's atom by the modern atomists. The size is roughly the same distance that light travels along its size.

Here, we recognise that Einstein's famous formula $E = mc^2$ is useful, where he claims mass is energy. As anybody experiences when he/she tries to divide some number by a very small number, 0 is very different from a non-zero number however small that number might be. Einstein considered $mc^2$ (with the velocity of light $c$) as the rest mass. When a particle moves, its energy is bigger than this rest mass energy. Because the rest mass is the smallest energy that the particle can possess, let us express energy as $E = mc^2$+(something) and measure the traversing time. The distance corresponding to the smallest energy, i.e. $E = mc^2$, is called the Compton wavelength to remember Arthur Compton who detected the electron scattered by light for the first time. For light, it is very strange. Light, radio waves, microwaves by which we receive TV broadcasts, X-rays, and gamma rays all travel with the same velocity, 380,000 km/s, at the sea level in England and Korea. Einstein gives the velocity or momentum of a particle as $p = \sqrt{E^2 - mc^2}/c$, which is the same as $E = mc^2$+(something). Since all kinds of electromagnetic waves travel with velocity $c$, mass of light or more generally mass of electromagnetic waves must be zero. The exact zero mass has a great significance, as will be discussed further in Chapter 8. The time measured by light travel has a physical significance. If a particle has mass $m$ and has an extended Compton wavelength size $\lambda_c$, the time required to traverse the particle is $\lambda_c/c$, and Compton defined the distance in terms of just one number, the rest mass.

In 1925, the Zeeman effect that Bohr's energy levels are split when atoms are placed in the magnetic fields was known. In classical mechanics, as mentioned above, angular momentum is calculable if $x$ and $p$ are known. This orbital angular momentum was used in Bohr's quantisation rules. In Bohr's model, therefore, there was no way to interpret the Zeeman effect. Thus, Samuel Gouldsmidt and George Uhlenbeck introduced a new kind of angular momentum which later was called as *spin* by Wolfgang Pauli in the Pauli–Schrödinger equation. An electron carries $\frac{\hbar}{2}$ unit and a photon carries $\hbar$ unit of this spin angular momentum. Usually, we simply write the electron and photon spins as $\frac{1}{2}$ and 1 without $\hbar$. In 1927, Paul Dirac (August 8, 1902–October 20, 1984) extended the Pauli–Schrödinger equation into a relativistic form, the Dirac equation. It is said that Paul Dirac came from Heaven down to Earth just to do physics.[11]

The Compton wavelength of the electron is about $2 \times 10^{-11}$ cm, roughly 250 times smaller than the size of a hydrogen atom. So, when one discusses the total angular momentum looking at the hydrogen atom, he/she must also consider the spin angular momentum of electron. That effect was what Goudsmit and Uhlenbeck suggested to explain the Zeeman effect. It was before the establishment of quantum mechanics. If a fundamental particle is considered as a point, the spin angular momentum is fundamentally different from the one obtained from some orbital motion. Spin must be an intrinsic property of a fundamental particle as shown for a counterclockwise sense of rotation (called L for left-handed in Fig. 3(b)) or a clockwise sense of rotation (called R for right-handed in Fig. 3(b)).

If we consider two waves, $\Psi(A)_i$ that $A$ located at $i$ and $\Psi(B)_j$ that $B$ located at $j$, we consider (number of possible $A$)×(number of possible $B$) wave functions. If two kinds are available for both $A$ and $B$, then there are four possibilities: $\Psi(A_1)_i\Psi(B_1)_j$, $\Psi(A_1)_i\Psi(B_2)_j$, $\Psi(A_2)_i\Psi(B_1)_j$, and $\Psi(A_2)_i\Psi(B_2)_j$, which are shown in Fig. 5. Here, the red and blue bullets denote two different wave functions. The first is the location $i$ and the second is the location $j$. For a spin-$\frac{1}{2}$ wave, the eigenvalues are either $+\frac{1}{2}$ or $-\frac{1}{2}$. If one consider two spin-$\frac{1}{2}$ waves, the eigenvalues are either $+1, 0$ or $-1$. The four possible cases are split into Figs. 5(a) and 5(b). For the $z$-component spin value of 0, there are the antisymmetric (a) and symmetric (b) combinations. If the same position is considered, $i = j$, then the antisymmetric combination vanishes. The spin-$\frac{1}{2}$ electron wave of antisymmetric combination is excluded. This is the essence of the Pauli exclusion principle in filling up atomic energy levels. Pauli was the father of the spin-statistics theorem that the half-integer spin particles, the so-called fermions, satisfy the Fermi–Dirac

[11] G. Farmelo, *The Strangest Man: The Hidden Life of Paul Dirac, The Mystic of Atom*, (Basic Books, New York, 2009). The words on his gravestone are "... because God made in that way...."

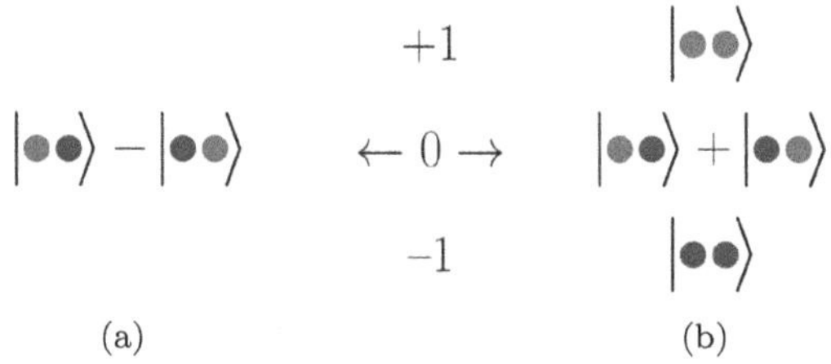

$$|\bullet\bullet\rangle - |\bullet\bullet\rangle \qquad \begin{matrix} +1 \\ \leftarrow 0 \rightarrow \\ -1 \end{matrix} \qquad \begin{matrix} |\bullet\bullet\rangle \\ |\bullet\bullet\rangle + |\bullet\bullet\rangle \\ |\bullet\bullet\rangle \end{matrix}$$

(a) (b)

Figure 5: Product of two wave functions.

statistics and the integer spin particles, the so-called bosons, satisfy the Bose–Einstein statistics. The Fermi–Dirac statistics chooses the antisymmetric combination and the Bose–Einstein statistics chooses the symmetric combination in Fig. 5. This spin-statistics theorem played an important role in finding quantum chromodynamics (QCDs) in the current atomic theory.

The relativistic formulation of quantum mechanics of electrons interacting with photons was written again by Paul Dirac in 1928, and is called quantum electrodynamics (QEDs). Since it describes the electron and photon waves, it is called quantum field theory of QED. Quantum fields (equal to waves supplemented by creation and annihilation operators satisfying Heisenberg's uncertainty relation; thus quantum) also contain antiparticles, and in particular, Dirac predicted the antiparticle of electron, *positron*. In 1929, Dmitri Skobeltsyn detected positron that acted like electrons but curved in the opposite direction in an applied magnetic field.

Around this time, nuclear beta decay showed peculiar behaviour with the knowledge of the time. Beta decay was first observed by Henri Becquerel in uranium in 1896. Beta decays are the result of weak interactions as we know now; these are one of the main focus points probing modern atomic theory, but the story went through many hurdles. The first important idea was on the prediction of neutrino(s) by Wolfgang Pauli. James Chadwick observed the continuous energy spectrum of beta rays in 1914, which posed the problem "Why?". At that time, nucleus, beta ray, and photon were the particles to be considered. In beta ray, photon is not considered. So, the continuous spectrum was a problem. There was an idea that the nuclear levels cascade down to lower states emitting photons, but in any case, there must be a primary electron which will kick out more electrons from outer shells of nucleus, which was not observed. Actually, it was puzzling enough that Niels Bohr suggested energy non-conservation only in beta decays. The nitrogen anomaly of that time was that $^7$N did not show Fermi statistics but Bose statistics (remember this time was before knowing the existence of neutron), i.e. Bose and Fermi statistics of nuclei at that time was determined by the charge number. In the nucleus model of that present, it was a dilemma and somehow Pauli knew the spin-statistics problem at that time. In 1929, Pauli was the Professor of Physics at the ETH Zurich, which might have been a centre of quantum mechanics then since people there then included Paul Dirac, Walter Heitler, Fritz London, Francis Wheeler Loomis, John von Neumann, John Slater, Leó Szilárd, Eugene Wigner, with Robert Oppenheimer and Isidor Rabi visiting there in March. At this time with his influential position, Pauli made the idea on *neutrino* public by writing a letter to the German Physical Society at Tübingen on December 4, 1930, "Dear Radioactive Ladies and Gentlemen, ... "wrong" statistics of the N and $^6$Li nuclei and the continuous beta spectrum, I have hit upon a desperate remedy to save the exchange theorem of statistics and the laws of conservation of energy. Namely, the possibility that there could exist in the nuclei electrically neutral particles, that I wish to call neutrons,[12] which have spin-$\frac{1}{2}$ and obey the exclusion principle ... that neutron at rest is a magnetic dipole of a certain moment $\mu$. The experiment seems to require that the effect of the ionisation of such a neutron cannot be larger than that of a gamma-ray and then $\mu$ should not be larger than $e \cdot 10^{-3}\,\text{cm}$ ... it would have a penetrating power similar to, or about 10 times larger than, a $\gamma$-ray." Obviously, he introduced an interaction[13] responsible for the decay by $\mu$, the magnetic moment interaction. But, Pauli's number is $10^8$ times the Bohr magneton which translates to $10^{16}$ times larger

[12]After neutron was discovered, Pauli's particle was called *neutrino*.

[13]It was the time before Fermi's writing of the weak interaction Hamiltonian.

rate if the Bohr magneton were used. Anyway, he considered his particle heavy, not the light one that we consider now.

Pauli's neutrino was observed in 1956, 36 years after Pauli suggested, by Frederick Reines and Clyde Cowan, working in Hanford and Savannah River Sites. Reines and Cowan developed the equipment and procedures with which they first detected the supposedly undetectable neutrinos on June 14, 1956, by placing a detector within a large antineutrino flux from a nearby nuclear reactor. Now, it is known that there are three neutrino species: the electron-type $\nu_e$, the muon-type $\nu_\mu$, and the tau-type $\nu_\tau$. These neutrinos transform to each other via the process known as *neutrino oscillation*. Unlike electron, muon, tau, and other coloured particles in Fig. 5 of Chapter 6, neutrinos are just two-component waves, the half of the others.

For 15 years between 1930 and 1945, there was not much theoretical progress. But here we note a very important discovery: the identification of another nucleon *neutron* by James Chadwick (1891–1974) in 1932, which guided the route to our current understanding of nucleus. Chadwick worked under Hans Geiger (1882–1945) several years since 1913. Acquainting with new technologies first is a guaranteed step towards new discoveries. The Geiger counter in 1913 provided more accuracy than earlier photographic techniques. In 1914, using the Geiger counter, Chadwick was able to demonstrate that beta radiation produced a continuous spectrum, as mentioned before, which led to Pauli's suggestion of neutrino. At the time around 1925 when spin was already known, it was believed that the nucleus core consisted of protons and electrons. So, nitrogen's nucleus with a mass number of 14 was assumed to contain 14 protons and 7 electrons. This gave it the right mass and charge, but the wrong spin ($14 + 7 = 21 =$ odd number) as mentioned above by Pauli (note that neutron was not counted at that time and hence only the atomic number mattered).

Acquaintance with Geiger enabled Chadwick knew a better detector early enough in this period. In 1928, he was introduced to the more powerful Geiger–Miller counter. Because of the problems in beta decays, Chadwick and Ernest Rutherford (1871–1937) had been hypothesising a theoretical nuclear particle with no electric charge (the neutron) for years.[14] If 7 "neutrons" are in the nitrogen nucleus in addition to 7 protons, the mass and charge of the nitrogen nucleus are explained. Then, the spin of the nitrogen nucleus would be even and the spin-statistics problem is satisfied. The major drawback with the earlier Geiger counter was that it detected alpha, beta and gamma radiation. The Cavendish laboratory where Chadwick and Rutherford worked in 1928 normally used the earlier Geiger counter in its experiments with radium. Radium emitted all three and was therefore unsuitable for what Chadwick had in mind for a theoretical nuclear particle with no electric charge. Polonium is an alpha emitter, and Lise Meitner sent Chadwick about 2 millicuries (about 0.5 g) from Germany.

In January 1932, Frédéric and Irène Joliot-Curie had succeeded in knocking protons from paraffin wax using polonium and beryllium as a source for what they thought was gamma radiation emitter. Rutherford and Chadwick disagreed; protons were too heavy for gamma radiation to push out (earlier, we commented that the heavy mass is needed for the collision effect to be large). But their theoretical nuclear particles with no electric charge would need only a small amount of energy to achieve the same effect. In Rome, Ettore Majorana came to the same conclusion. In retrospect, Frédéric and Irène Joliot-Curie had discovered the neutron, but did not know it. This reminds us that even experimentalists must have enough common sense on theoretical ideas.

To Chadwick, this was evidence of something that he and Rutherford had been hypothesising for years. Chadwick dropped all his other responsibilities to concentrate on proving the existence of the neutron. He devised a cylinder containing a polonium source and beryllium target and the suitable detection apparatus. In February 1932, after only about two weeks of experimentation, Chadwick confirmed his idea and sent the paper to *Nature* with the title "Possible Existence of a Neutron". This was a rough sketch of how *neutron* was discovered and revolutionalised nuclear physics, and we

---

[14] A. Brown, *The Neutron and the Bomb: A Biography of Sir James Chadwick* (Oxford University Press, 1997); ISBN 978-0-19-853992-6.

remember Rutherford the father of nuclear physics and Chadwick the discoverer of neutron.

In 1933, Chadwick and Goldhaber showed by experiment that the neutron is slightly more massive than the proton which is an important fact for various reasons, e.g. it enables the weak interaction $\beta$-decay of a neutron into a proton.

In 1934, Fermi proposed his theory of beta decay which explained that the electrons emitted from the nucleus were essentially by the decay of a neutron into a proton, an electron, and an antineutrino. Fermi's weak interaction Hamiltonian contained effectively 34 terms. On December 17, 1938, German Otto Hahn (1879–1968) and Fritz Strassmann (1902–1980) found the nuclear fission and nuclear reaction: A heavy nucleus spontaneously or by collision by a neutron split into two lighter nuclei. Nuclear reaction of a heavy nucleus, e.g. uranium 235, was used in early engineered nuclear devices. The available energy, enormous energy compared to energy from chemical reactions, was used in atomic bomb and later in nuclear reactors, currently supplying substantial portion of electric power in France, Japan, Korea, etc. One class of nuclear weapon, a fission bomb or atomic bomb, is a fission reactor designed to liberate as much energy as possible and as rapidly as possible.

Ettore Majorana (1906–1938?), mentioned above, disappeared very mysteriously. Nobody has seen him after he took off Palermo by ship to Naples on March 25, 1938. Since 1963, Italians commemorate him hosting schools in Erice (near Palermo), Sicily, mainly organized by high-energy experimentalist Antonino Zichichi (1929–), and in the booming period of gauge theories, important lectures were given in Erice.

But, his name is mostly cited these days on the nature of neutrinos. A massless neutral two-component spin-$\frac{1}{2}$ particle is called either a Weyl or a Majorana particle. If exactly massless, it does not matter which name we use. But, if it is massive, they are physically different.

Pauli considered two spin states of Fig. 3 and put the two states as a $2 \times 1$ column matrix and called it spinor. Then, the spinor wave function has two complex components and is called a doublet **2** in group theory. The non-relativistic Schrödinger equation satisfied by $\Psi_2$ is the Pauli–Schrödinger equation. Dirac generalized it to a relativistic form by combining with another spinor, effectively including the antiparticle. The non-vanishing mass makes all the four complex components be used. But, if mass is zero, consideration of two complex components is enough.

Out of the four complex components, there are two possibilities for reducing them to half, among which Majorana chose the case that the four complex components are reduced to half just by considering the four real comonents. The Dirac equation satisfied by the four real components is the Majorana equation satisfied by a Majorana particle. Choosing just the reality condition allows non-zero mass for a Majorana particle. The other way, reducing the four complex components to two complex components, gives the 'Weyl' spinor which cannot be realized if mass is non-zero. To make up mass by Weyl spinors, two Weyl spinors are needed. Since neutrino masses are known to be non-zero, it is important to check whether they are of Majorana type or Dirac type.

Hideki Yukawa (1907–1981) was a Japanese theoretical physicist and the first Japanese Nobel laureate known for his prediction of the pi meson. After receiving his degree from Kyoto Imperial University in 1929, he stayed there as a lecturer for 4 years and then moved to Osaka Imperial University as Assistant Professor. There, he proposed the pion as the mediator of the nuclear forces. In 1940, he won the Imperial Prize of the Japan Academy, and in 1949, he was awarded the Nobel Prize in Physics after the discovery of pions by Cecil Frank Powell, H. Muirhead, Giuseppe Occhialini and César Lattes of Yukawa's predicted charged and neutral pi mesons $(\pi^{\pm}, \pi^0)$ in 1947. The masses of these pi mesons are (139.6 MeV, 135.0 MeV).

In 1935, Yukawa published his theory of mesons in the *Proceedings of Japanese Mathematical Society*,[15] considering a charged scalar particle (with a fortunate sign mistake). He showed that its mass

[15]H. Yukawa, On the Interactions of Elementary Particles I, *Proceedings of Japanese Mathematical Society* **17**, 48–57 (1935) [*Progress of Theoretical Physics Supplements* **1**, 1–10 (1955) [doi.org/10.1143/PTPS.1.1]].

must be about 200 times electron mass, which was a major influence on the research into elementary particles. Yukawa's group at Osaka, including Sakata, Taketani, and Fushimi, intensively developed the theory of mesons. Yukawa argued that there must be not only charged bosons but also neutral boson. In 1937–1938, he believed that vector bosons are better than scalar bosons to explain spectrum and properties of nuclei. According to Yutaka Hosotani, the neutral pseudoscalar pion was realized much later.

Yukawa's meson potential is the beginning of the study of forces by exchanges of integer-spin particles. It is like considering two figure-skate players exchanging a basketball as they skate, as shown in Fig. 6(a). When the skater A tosses the basketball, his trajectory shifts a bit to compensate the momentum carried by the basketball, satisfying the momentum conservation. When the skater B receives and tosses back the ball, his trajectory shifts a bit by the same argument. Continuous exchanges of the ball ends up hyperbolic trajectories of both skaters A and B. Observers looking at A's and B's trajectories would consider that there is a repulsive force between them. Yukawa mimiced this repulsive force by introducing unnoticeable mediator *basketball* in this case. In the modern jargon, the mediator is an elementary particle *pion*, which is depicted as the propagator in the Feynman diagram in Fig. 6(b).

The force law obtained in this way is exponentially suppressed related to the mass of exchanging particle. Because nuclear forces in the nucleus do not extend beyond the nuclear size, Yukawa predicted the mass of pion to be around 200 times the electron mass. If the mass of the exchanged particle is heavy, the trajectory is more curved

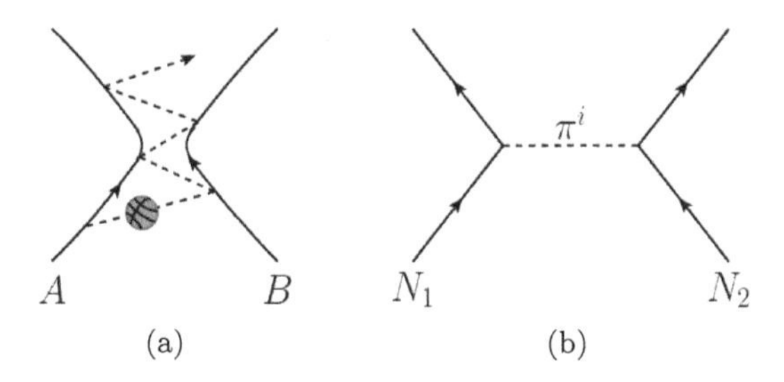


Figure 6: An idea of Yukawa's pion.

compared to a light particle exchange. One can understand that exchange of a ping-pong ball may not affect the curving of the trajectory very much. The same happens in the world of atoms. If a low-energy photon is exchanged, the trajectories are almost in the forward direction. In this sense, the UA1/UA2 experiments of 1982 in discovering $Z^0$ and $W^\pm$ bosons and the recent LHC experiments looked for hard collision events to find heavy particles.

But, the above explanation misses one important fact. Figure 6(a) describes a replusive force while we need an attractive force for binding protons and neutrons strongly inside a nucleus. So, it is better for A and B to be connected by a rope. From time to time, A and B attract the rope such that they come closer. The oscillation of the rope may be considered as a wave describing the exchanged particle. More technically, exchange of a spin-0 particle always gives an attractive force. For spin-1 particle, such as photon, it can give repulsive or attractive force, depending on the relative charges of the two particles. Furthermore, in a more technical jargon, the spin-0 particle appearing in relation to the unitary group is always "pseudoscalar". So, what Yukawa predicted was a pseudoscalar triplet, $\pi^\pm, \pi^0$, a representation of the unitary group SU(2).

As in many other cases, this intermediate particle idea was also considered by another physicist. It was by Swiss mathematician and physicist, Baron Ernst Carl Gerlach Stückelberg von Breidenbach zu Breidenstein und Melsbac (1905–1984), who is regarded as one of the most eminent physicists of the 20th century. Stückelberg's sojourn in Zurich in 1932 led to contact with leading quantum theorists Wolfgang Pauli and Gregor Wentzel, which in turn led him to focus on the emerging theory of elementary particles. Stückelberg's intermediary was a massive spin-1 particle, and he discussed his idea with Wolfgan Pauli who immediately rejected the idea. When we assess why Pauli objected to Stückelberg's idea immediately, we note that it is because Pauli was the guru understanding gauge forces. With spin-1 particle exchange, big nucleus is full of repulsive protons, and hence, he might not have agreed to Stückelberg's idea.

Yukawa's original idea was exactly like Stückelberg's spin-1. But, Yukawa was lucky. He submitted the idea to *Physical Review*, for which Robert Oppenheimer was the Editor at that time. Oppenheimer considered it being submitted from a backward country not knowing physics (at that time) and rejected it outright.[16] So, Yukawa's wrong idea was not published. Nevertheless, he continued with pseudoscalar intermediary, which we call pions now. Six months after rejecting Yukawa's wrong idea, Oppenheimer considered that Yukawa's idea was not that bad actually and felt sorry for his rejection for a long time. This might be one reason that he recommended Yukawa to the Nobel Committee in 1949.

In 1936, right after Yukawa's suggestion of pions, Carl Anderson (1895–1991) and Seth Neddermeyer (1907–1988) at Caltech observed particles heavier than electron and lighter than proton from cosmic rays.[17] They noted particles that curved differently from electrons and were negatively charged but curved less sharply than electrons, but more sharply than protons. Thus, Anderson initially called the new particle a mesotron, adopting the prefix *meso-* from the Greek word for "mid-".[18] Initially, it was considered as the pion that Yukawa suggested, just from the mass region. But, the single long track did not look like a strongly interacting pion. The existence of this deeply penetrating particle was confirmed in 1937 by J. C. Street and E. C. Stevenson's cloud chamber experiment.[19] Now, it is called muon.

Before the end of WWII, only photon, electron and muon were discovered among the fundamental particles of the Standard Model shown in Fig. 5 of Chapter 6.

---

[16]Susumu Okubo's comment to the second author at Rochester, New York, January, 2010.
[17]C. D. Anderson and S. Neddermeyer, New Evidence for the Existence of a Particle of Mass Intermediate Between the Proton and Electron, *Physical Review* **52**, 1003 (1937).
[18]This prefix transferred to Yukawa's pions. Now, mesons mean strongly interacting bosons, including pions and other bosons made of a quark and an antiquark.
[19]J. Street and E. Stevenson, New Evidence for the Existence of a Particle of Mass Intermediate Between the Proton and Electron, *Physical Review* **52**, 1003 (1937).

## Chapter 6

# Particle Theory

In 1942, the wartime Manhattan Project gathered the US talents in nuclear physics at Los Alamos, New Mexico. The project, led by Major General Leslie Groves (1896–1970) and theoretical physicist Robert Oppenheimer (1904–1967), succeeded in making the atomic bomb which was tested in the New Mexico Desert at 5:30 a.m. on July 16, 1945 with an energy equivalent of around 20 kilotons of TNT, having left a crater called Trinitite. Many nuclear physicists who participated in the Manhattan Project opened the field of *particle physics or high energy physics.*

After WWII, Oppenheimer joined The Institute for Advanced Study at Princeton as the director. He convened 25 leading physicists at Ram's Head Inn on Shelter Island near the tip of Long Island, New York, for a one-day conference on June 1, 1947. Some participants were Willis Lamb, Richard Feynman, Julian Schwinger, Hans Bethe, Enrico Fermi, and Robert Marshak. The main topic of interest at this conference was the observation of the Lamb shift. At this time, the accepted particle theory was quantum electrodynamics (QED), formulated by Paul Dirac in 1928. But, these talented physicists could not explain the Lamb shift.

Oppenheimer's conference continued at Pocono Manor, Pocono Mountains, Pennsylvania, in 1948 and at Oldstone-on-Hudson near New York in 1949. From the beginning of this series, the infinity first encountered in the explanation of the Lamb shift was the hurdle to be overcome. In the 1948 meeting, Schwinger presented a largely completed work, and Feynman's exposition known as Feynman diagrams (largely orchestrated by Oppenheimer) was presented at the 1949 meeting. By this time, QED was able to present refined calculations of electron interactions mediated by photons. So, Oppenheimer achieved his goal of understanding the original infinities in QED and finished his conferences.

Robert Oppenheimer was known to be a philanthropist, a genius, and a poet as noticed from comments after his death: the Times of London described him as the quintessential "Renaissance man", and his friend David Lilienthal told the *New York Times*, "The world has lost a noble spirit — a genius who brought together poetry and science." Also, in 1963 on the occasion of Fermi Prize award, CBS broadcaster Eric Sevareid described him as "the scientist who writes like a poet and speaks like a prophet." He died on February 18, 1967, and the urn of his ashes was lowered into Hawksnest Bay, St. John, Virgin Island. He opened the window toward modern-day atomic theory.

By 1949, as mentioned above, interactions between electrons and photons were completely understood in terms of QED. The calculation of the magnetic moment of electron in QED is 1.001 159 652 181 64 ($\pm$76), while the observed value is 1.001 159 652 180 91 ($\pm$26). So, the QED accuracy is correct up to 1 part in 1,000,000,000,000, and is the most successful scientific theory. Since 1949, numerous strongly interacting particles had been observed. The well-known one is the pion mentioned earlier. This pion and the related strong interaction were not understood in 1949. It was a problem to understand pions and related particles.

For the purpose of understanding pions and other strongly interacting particles, the first Rochester Conference was organised by Robert Marshak, then Chairman of Physics at the University of Rochester, and held on December 16, 1950. The next several Rochester Conferences witnessed the cradle of particle physics: discussions on the tau–theta puzzle, parity violation, and the so-called "V–A" theory in weak interactions. In the session presided by Oppenheimer on "Theoretical Interpretatioin of New Particles" on the last day of Rochester-6 (1956),[1] the puzzle related to the tau and theta particles was the main topic. After Chen Ning Yang's talk, Feynman brought up a question of Block's, "Could it be that the tau and theta are different parity states of the same particle which has no definite parity, i.e. parity is not conserved?"

During ICHEP-6, Feynman shared a room with Martin Block (1925–2016), and one evening Block said to Feynman, as was written in *Surely You Are Joking*,[2] "Why are you guys so insistent on this parity rule? Maybe the tau and theta are the same particle. What would be the consequences if the parity rules were wrong?"

The solution of the tau–theta puzzle was that weak interactions, in the nuclear beta decays, in hyperon decays, and in the decays of mesons, in general do not respect the space inversion symmetry, called the "parity" operation. In late 1956, the parity violation in weak interactions was suggested by Tsung Dao Lee (1926–) and Chen Ning Yang (1922–). Parity violation is the unique feature in the weak force among the four known forces: electromagnetic, weak, strong, and gravitational forces. The Lee and Yang paper raised the important experimental question of whether weak interactions were parity invariant, meaning that they would be the same if the experiment were reflected in a mirror. Yang has told the first author that they did not expect parity to be violated, and indeed Lee and Yang changed their research interest to statistical mechanics. Nevertheless, they were surprised and delighted when the experiment of Madame Chien-Shiung Wu (1912–1997) and collaborators showed that parity was maximally violated in weak interactions. The experiment involved studying the $\beta$-decay of polarised Cobalt-60 nuclei, as suggested to Lee and Yang by Maurice Goldhaber (1911–2011). This result was

---

[1] J. Polkinghorne, *Rochester Roundabout* (R. H. Freeman and Company, New York, 1989), and Inspires C56-04-03, *Proceedings of 6th ICHEP*, Rochester, New York, USA, April 3–7, 1956.

[2] R. Leighton and E. Hutchings (editors) *Surely You're Joking, Mr. Feynman!: Adventures of a Curious Character* (W W Norton, New York, 1985), ISBN 0-393-01921-7.

a surprise to most physicists and did lead to the award of a Nobel Prize immediately in 1957. The parity violation in weak interactions opened a new field: particle physics. Before 1957, there was no word "particle physics".

After 1957, particle physicists differentiated from the study of nuclear physics, looking for much shorter distance scales compared to the nuclear size, i.e. paying much more attention to higher energy scales. This is the reason particle physics is synonymous with high-energy physics (HEP), and the international conference of particle physics is called ICHEP.

After it was accepted that parity is violated in the charged current (CC) weak interactions, Rochester-7 was short of announcing the "V–A" theory of CC weak interactions. There is an anecdote at Rochester-7 that George Sudarshan, a graduate student at Rochester, asked Robert Marshak to present their recently completed idea of "V–A" theory of weak interactions. But, Marshak as the chairman of the LOC did not allow his talk, replying that Martin Block was supposed to mention their work. But, Block did not appear, so Marshak presented their work at the Padova conference four months later. Between Rochester-7 and 8, it was advocated by Marshak, Sudarshan, Feynman, and Gell-Mann that the CC weak interactions chose only the "V–A" part but never "V+A". These four famous physicists are the "V–A" quartet. From this time on, only one coupling constant $G_F$ has been used for all the CC weak interactions out of Enrico Fermi's 34 constants, and developments in particle physics have been possible from this time on, finding symmetries required for understanding weak and strong interactions at the level of QED. This "V–A" theory was the cornerstone to the road to the Standard Model (SM) and Shoichi Sakata's symmetry was the beginning in the search for strong interaction symmetries. However, there is one more hurdle to be overcome, which is discussed in more detail in Chapter 7.

The year 1964 was a creative year. Then, Gell-Mann's mathematical quark (or Zweig's Ace) loomed in his cherished eight-fold way of currents, the weak CP violation was observed by the Princeton group, and the Brout–Englert–Higgs–Guralnik–Hagen–Kibble (BEHGHK) mechanism, the Higgs mechanism in short, was known. A year later in 1965, an additional SU(3) degree (later known as colour) for strong interactions was proposed by Moo-Young Han and Yoichiro Nambu. Gell-Mann's mathematical quark and colour SU(3) were accepted ten years later at the November Revolution of 1974. The BEHGHK mechanism was finally proved by the discovery of the 125 GeV boson in 2012. For the weak CP violation phenomena, it was in 2006 that three families of quarks in the SM were considered enough to explain them all. During this crucial period, the ICHEP-12 was held in a small town Dubna, on the banks of Volga River, USSR (August 5–12, 1964). Val Fitch (1923–2015) brought and showed his Princeton apparatus, which had discovered the weak CP violation. It was a period when tabletop experiments could reveal important aspects of particle interactions.

The BEHGHK mechanism was known in 1964, but even in the ICHEP-13 Berkeley in 1966, plenary sessions did not include spontaneous symmetry breaking. The year 1967 was the year for this to get attention[3] in the conference (with 325 theorists participating) dedicated to the late Robert Oppenheimer, who passed away on February 18, 1967, which is considered to be the commencement year of the SM by representing the quark and lepton doublets only in the left-handed sector by Steven Weinberg, realising the "V–A" nature of the weak CC formulated in 1957 by "V–A" quartet. But, the SM needed a few more years to bloom until the renormalisability of the spontaneously broken gauge theories was proven in 1971 by Gerard 't Hooft (1946–) and Martinus Veltman (1931–). The ICHEP series expanded since the ICHEP-16 Chicago, which was held at Fermilab during September 6–13, 1972, with the number of participants exceeding 300.

As mentioned in the end of Chapter 5, there were two similar particles known before the end of WWII: electron and muon. Muons

[3]T. W. B. Kibble, The Goldstone theorem, in Particles and Fields, *Proc. of "International Conference on Particles and Fields*, Rochester, N.Y., U. S. A., August 28–September 1, 1967, eds. G. S. Guralnik, C. R. Hagen and V. S. Mathur (Interscience, New York, NY, 1968), pp. 277–295.

behaved exactly the same way as electrons in QED and weak interactions except for their mass difference. This repetition problem was succinctly expressed as "Who ordered that?" by Isidor Issac Rabi (1898–1988) of Columbia University in 1937 in response to the news that the 1936-discovered muon was not a hadron but a new and entirely unexpected type of lepton. Still, this was the culminating phrase on the current *flavour problem* or the *family problem*. The question on the difference of electron and muon masses was one of the flavour problems. It is said that in the United States of America, Oppenheimer was the first theoretician and Rabi was the first experimentalist understanding quantum mechanics. Rabi and Oppenheimer were good friends since 1929, as mentioned earlier, and went to Zürich together, and maintained their friendship through their lifetime during the Manhattan Project years and afterward also. Another Rabi quip is "We have an A-bomb and a whole series of it, and what do you want, mermaids?" to the Atomic Energy Commission, defending Oppenheimer against charges of leaking classified information during the McCarthyism era.[4]

A legacy of the Manhattan Project led by Oppenheimer was the network of researchers in the United States, but no national laboratory comparable to the one at Los Alamos was located on the East Coast of the United States. Isidor Rabi and Norman Ramsey, both at Columbia University, assembled a group of universities in the New York area to lobby for their own national laboratory. Rabi had discussions with Major General Leslie Groves, whom he knew from the Manhattan Project, who was willing to go along with a new national laboratory. Moreover, while the Manhattan Project still had funds, the wartime organisation was expected to be phased out when a new authority came into existence. After some discussions, the two groups agreed in January 1946. Finally, nine universities (Columbia, Princeton, Rochester, Pennsylvania, Harvard, Cornell, MIT, Yale, and Johns Hopkins) came together, and on January 31, 1947, a contract was signed with the Atomic Energy Commission

[4]McCarthyism was the practice, during the cold war time of the early 1950s, of making accusations of subversion or treason without proper regard for evidence.

(AEC), which had replaced the Manhattan Project, that established the Brookhaven National Laboratory(BNL).[5] After establishing the BNL, Rabi suggested to Edoardo Amaldi (1908–1989) that BNL might be a model which Europeans could benchmark. Rabi saw science as a way of inspiring and uniting a Europe that was still recovering from the war. An opportunity came in 1950 when he was named the United States Delegate to the United Nations Educational, Scientific and Cultural Organization (UNESCO). At a UNESCO meeting at the Palazzo Vecchio in Florence in June 1950, he called for the establishment of regional laboratories. These efforts bore fruit; in 1952, representatives of eleven countries came together to create the Conseil Européen pour la Recherche Nucléaire (CERN). Rabi received a letter from Bohr, Heisenberg, Amaldi, and others congratulating him on the success of his efforts. Now, the bronze sculpture of Niels Bohr's face is displayed at the CERN Library. The Higgs boson in Fig. 5 was discovered at the LHC of CERN.

In 1963, one important flavour regularity on hadrons was observed by Italian physicist Nicola Cabibbo (1935–2010). He was considering decay rates triggered by the charged current (CC) weak interactions. A family of 15 chiral fields, which are mentioned at the end of this chapter, consists of three chiral leptons and twelve chiral quarks. Decays of particles such as the beta decay are going through the CC weak interactions. If there was only one family, there is only the decay of neutron and pion by the CC interaction. If there are two families, we can consider additional possibilities due to the addition of the second family, i.e. the decays of muon ($\mu$) and strange($s$)/charm($c$) particles as shown in Fig. 5. In 1963, charmed particles were not known. So, he compared rates of the muon decay, the beta or neutron decay, and the Lambda (= a strange baryon) decay, obtaining (muon decay rate) = (neutron decay rate) + (Lambda decay rate) after factoring out kinematic factors properly. If one squared value is the sum of two squared values, then it is the Pythagoras theorem for a right triangle, i.e. $1 = \cos^2\theta + \sin^2\theta$.

[5] J. C. Rigden, *Rabi, Scientist and Citizen* (Sloan Foundation Series, Basic Books, New York, 1987), ISBN 0-465-06792-1, OCLC 14931559.

We call this angle observed in the above CC weak interaction the Cabibbo *mixing* angle $\theta_C$, which is about 13°. When we say an angle, it appears naturally in some unitary transformation as mentioned before. Therefore, it is a quantum mechanical effect because two wave functions are mixed. In classical mechanics, one never considers mixing of two particles. The Cabibbo angle is for the case of mixing two waves, i.e., those of neutron and Lambda. In the quark model, it describes a mixing angle of $d$ and $s$ quarks. In 1963, the quark model was not known. But, the eight-fold way of currents in strong interactions shown in Fig. 1 was known chiefly by Murray Gell-Mann. Among these, the plus CCs are $(I_+ \equiv F_1 + iF_2)$ and $(V_+ \equiv F_4 + iF_5)$. So, quantum mechanics allows a unitary transformation, with the absolute magnitude 1 such that these two combinations are mixed. This combination appearing in $e^{iF_C\theta_C}$ is describing both beta decay and Lambda decay. On the contrary, the muon decay does not belong to the eight-fold way since there is no strongly interacting particle involved. Therefore, the corresponding unitary transformation is just a phase multiplication. Relation between these is basically $1 = \cos^2\theta_C + \sin^2\theta_C$. This was the reason that Cabibbo found the unitary transformation even before the advent of the quark model. In fact, Gell-Mann and Lévy included a footnote in their $\sigma$-model paper published in 1960 in the Italian journal *Nuovo Cimento*, "Of course, what really counts is the nature of the commutation relations for the *complete* operators that generate the sum of the $\Delta S = 0$ and $\Delta S = 1$

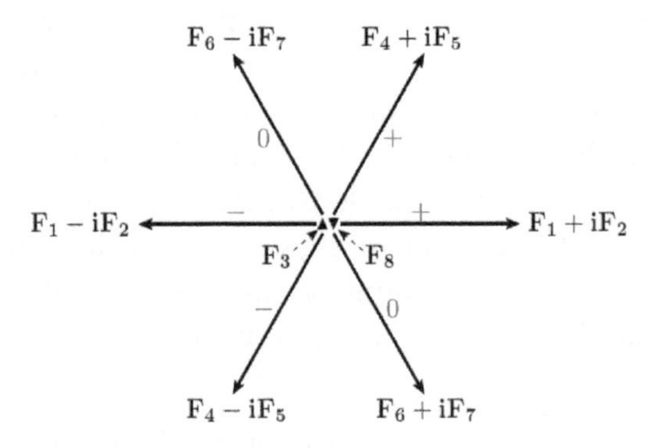


Figure 1: Eight-fold way of currents.

currents," where $S$ is the strangeness quantum number of hadrons. We may understand their "*complete* operators" as our one unitary operator, but it is not clear what they meant by *complete*. Gell-Mann and Lévy were to Cabibbo what Greek atomists were to Dalton, based on the accounts of the observed facts. After the quark model was proposed, this mixing effect is written as Cabibbo's mixed quark, mixing between the $d$ quark and the $s$ quark: $d' = d\cos\theta_C + s\sin\theta_C$.

In the eight-fold way in Fig. 1, there are four neutral currents, corresponding to $F_3, F_8, F_{6+i7}$, and $F_{6-i7}$. A magnitude 1 unitary transformation can be a combination of these four, but here $F_{6\pm i7}$ does not conserve the strangeness quantum number. At the weak interaction level with the Fermi constant $G_F$, the strangeness changing *neutral* current (SCNC) effects were not observed until 1970. So, there was a need to remove this SCNC. The answer was provided by Sheldon Glashow, John Iliopoulos, and Luciano Maiani (GIM) in 1970 by introducing an additional quark charm $c$, and by introducing another mixing between the $d$ and $s$ quarks: $s' = -d\sin\theta_C + s\cos\theta_C$. It is said that Ziro Maki and Yoshio Ohnuki introduced the fourth quark $c$ in 1964, but Maki and Ohnuki are to GIM what Greek atomists are to Dalton.

Earlier, we mentioned two mixing relations with one angle, $d'$ and $s'$. This case is succinctly written by four numbers to generate the unitary matrix of mixing $d$ and $s$ quarks in terms of one angle. The Cabibbo angle of 13 degrees, to make a unitary matrix, is implied by displaying a set of four numbers as shown in Fig. 2(a). If three quarks mix, we need three angles to discuss the quantum mechanical mixing of three quarks. In this case, we need an array of nine numbers as shown in Fig. 2(b). The SM has six quarks and we need mixing between only half of these quarks, i.e. $d$, $s$, and $b$ quarks or $u, c$, and $t$ quarks. Theoretically, not only the gauge interactions,

$$\begin{matrix} +0.970 & +0.242 \\ -0.242 & +0.970 \end{matrix}$$

(a)

$$\begin{matrix} +0.975 & +0.221 & +0.0039 \\ -0.221 & +0.974 & +0.0171 \\ -0.0082 & -0.018 & +0.999 \end{matrix}$$

(b)

Figure 2: Arrays of numbers.

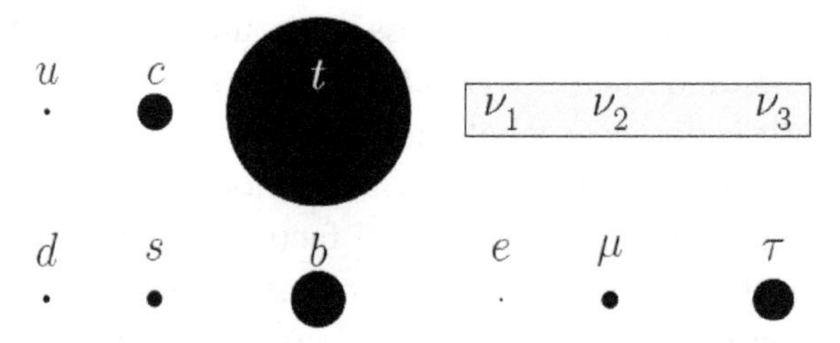


Figure 3: Relative sizes of masses. The masses of neutrinos are so small compared to the electron mass, at least a hundred-millionth, their sizes cannot be shown in the figure. In the yellow band, it is only shown that there are three small masses.

as discussed above in terms of currents, but also the particle masses participate in physics of elementary particles, for example the Higgs boson interaction with quarks to render quarks massive. In sum, physics related to inter-family relations is called the family problem or the flavour problem.

The masses of quarks and leptons are schematically shown in Fig. 3. We notice that there is a hierarchy of masses of order hundred million between the electron and top quark. As noticed from Figs. 2 and 3, this flavour problem in the quark sector is a very difficult problem. So far, we looked for how Nature revealed its secret regularities to us but Figs. 2 and 3 seem to not hint at any simple regularity. The flavour problem is considered the most important remaining theoretical problem in the SM.

In the leptonic sector also, there are mixings. Since we already know that there are three families, let us discuss the mixing of three lepton families. Generalisation of the strangeness changing neutral current is the flavour[6] changing neutral current(FCNC). The absence of FCNC at order $G_F$ in the leptonic sector is also verified from the negligible rate for muon to electron plus photon, $\mu \to e + \gamma$, in the decay of muon. Since the flavour problem brings in the masses of each particle, the mass generating mechanism is important in the flavour

[6]The word "flavour" is used for distinguishing different particles which however have the same electroweak interactions, i.e., interactions mediated by photon, $Z$ and $W^{\pm}$ in Fig. 5. On the Contrary, "colour" is used for defining strong interaction.

problem or in understanding the observed number of arrays shown in Fig. 2. According to Einstein, mass is energy as known by his famous formula $E = mc^2$. Therefore, mixing must be considered with the energies under consideration: the kinetic energy and potential energy. At low energy, mass belongs to the potential energy. In the quark sector, the kinetic energies in the experiments we chose are much smaller, and the fact that mixing depending on mass is all we need to consider.

In the leptonic sector, let us choose masses such that $Q_{\rm em} = -e$ leptons are already diagonalised. And, we discuss three neutrinos of Fig. 3 without worrying about diagonalisation of charged leptons. The kinetic energies of the observed neutrinos vary over a wide range. Reines and Cowan's nuclear reactor electron antineutrinos are several MeVs. Lederman, Schwartz, and Steinberger's muon neutrinos from Alternating Gradient Synchrotron of BNL are 200 MeVs. Neutrinos for the T2K (Tokai to Kamioka) experiments used for the observation of the tau neutrinos are from the 50 GeV proton source at J-Park, Japan. All these kinetic energies are much larger than any mass of three neutrinos. So, the neutrino mixing, or the flavour mixing in the leptonic sector, is observed by the mixing effects in the kinetic energy of neutrinos. The kinetic energies are compared to the differences of neutrino mass energy. Calculations show that leading mixing effects (or neutrino oscillation) occur at the difference of squared neutrino masses $\Delta m^2$. In the mixing, we have angles which are dimensionless since they are arguments in the phase, and hence $\Delta m^2$ appears in the numerator in the phase since more mass difference gives faster oscillation. Therefore, we expect a dimensionless argument $\Delta m^2 \times$(distance travelled by neutrino)/(kinetic energy). This formula was first obtained by Russian physicist Bruno Pontecorvo in 1957 for the case of electron-type neutrino and antineutrino oscillation. Note that only the electron-type neutrino was known in 1956, and hence Pontecorvo considered the $\nu_e$ and $\bar{\nu}_e$ oscillation.

Oscillations of three neutrinos require three real angles by an array of the type shown in Fig. 2(b), but the leptonic sector gives a different set of numbers from the shape for the numbers corresponding to quarks. Since neutrino oscillation experiments depend on the distance travelled by neutrinos, there are short baseline experiments, long baseline experiments, and even the very long distance for Solar neutrinos. Two of the three vertical numbers of Fig. 2(b) were first obtained from cosmic ray neutrinos scattering with nuclei in the atmosphere. Short baseline experiments looking for relatively large differences of squared masses are done by placing detectors near nuclear reactors. The Raymond Davies (1914–2006) Solar neutrino problem was that he did not see as much electron neutrinos as calculated by theorists, notably by John Bahcall (1934–2005), through the nuclear fusion processes in the core of the Sun. On the contrary, long baseline experiments can see the effects of very small squared mass differences, enabling one to observe the CP violation better. Now, we discuss the CP violation observed in the quark and leptonic sectors.

We discussed three angles to represent mixing between three particles. These angles are called Euler angles, introduced by Leonhard Euler (1707–1783), to describe the relative orientation of two rigid bodies of the same shape. As shown in Fig. 4 where the centre of weight is at the origin, first rotate the solid around the axis $z$ by an angle $\alpha$, then around the axis $N$ by an angle $\beta$, and finally around

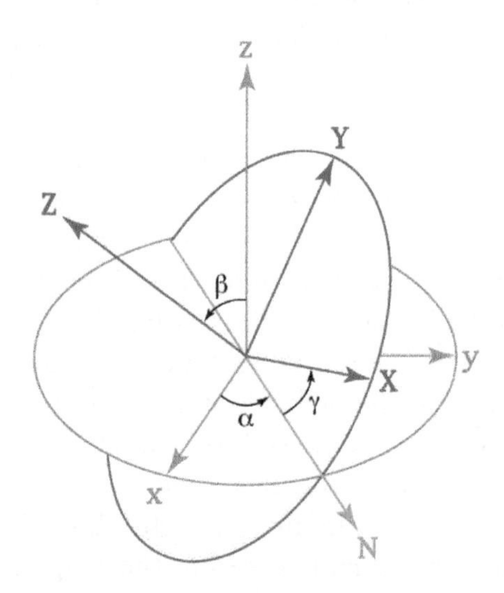


Figure 4: Proper Euler angles drawn by Lionel Brits in Wikipedia.

the axis $Z$ by an angle $\gamma$. The angles $\alpha, \beta$, and $\gamma$ are called three Euler angles.

Mixing in terms of only real angles cannot describe the CP violation. Here, C is the transformation of a particle to an antiparticle such as changing an electron to a positron. P is the inversion of spatial coordinates. If $\mathbf{x}$ denotes the three coordinates of a particle, change its position to $-\mathbf{x}$: it is parity $P$. The combined operation, changing a particle to its antiparticle with the inverted coordinates, is the CP transformation on the particle. Forces or interactions acting on paricles are the roles of spin-1 particles in the second annulus in Fig. 5. There is no confusion describing photon as a real particle. Quantum mechanical transformation is a unitary transformation, and hence a photon does not change to another by C. For that matter, gluons behave in the same way. So, gluons also respect C. For the inversion of coordinates, it is known in the history of QED since 1928 that it respects P. The effect of neutral currents is flavour conserving and we do not pay attention to the interactions resulting from $Z$ of Fig. 5, without worries about the FCNC effects. Gluons behave in the same way as QED at the tree level.[7] There remain the effects of $W^{\pm}$ interactions, i.e. those of CCs of matter fermions. Since CCs are defined only for the triangled fermions in Fig. 5, C and P are violated and there is no argument at this stage against CP violation in the CC weak interaction. If antiparticles behave exactly in the same way with the real number set of Fig. 2(b), then there is no way to decide whether we are looking at particles or antiparticles. To have a difference in the particle and antiparticle interactions due to $W^{\pm}$, there must be an additional parameter. It must be a phase since the role of three Euler angles is completed by three real angles. A phase must appear in the array of Fig. 2(b). This possibility was found by Mokoto Kobayashi and Toshihide Maskawa in 1972. Namely, a phase $e^{i\delta}$ appears at some entries in Fig. 2(b). Similarly, if a phase appears in the leptonic number arrays, then there is the weak CP violation in the neutrino oscillation.

[7]If we consider loop effects, there are violation of P in gluon interactions, which lead to the so-called strong CP problem.

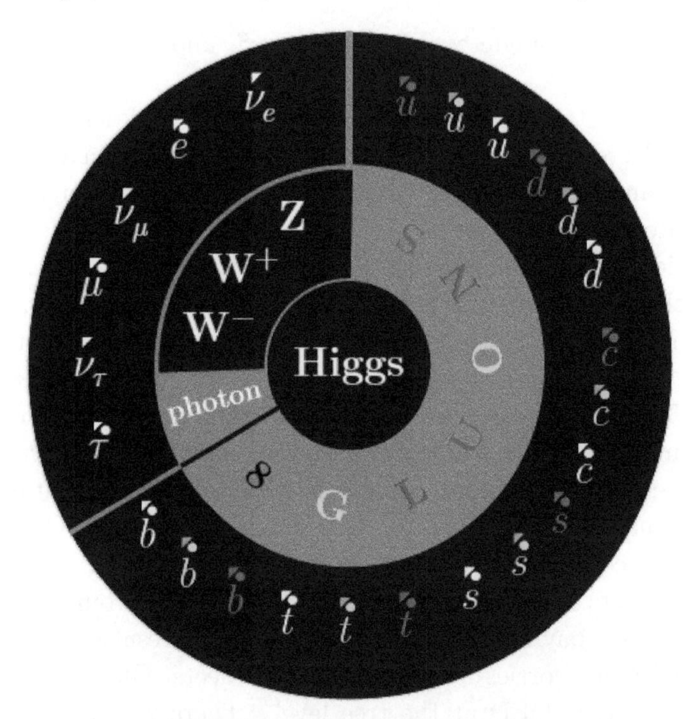


Figure 5: Particles in the SM. Particles on the grey disk are massless, and all the other particles obtain mass due to the Higgs boson. Quarks are repeated three times, which is symbolised by red, green, and yellow. White particles do not carry colour. Helicities are denoted by triangle for L-handed and bullet for R-handed. Neutrinos have only the L-handed helicity.

Let us list all the fundamental particles of the SM in Fig. 5. Any particle beyond those in Fig. 5 is a beyond-the-Standard-Model (BSM) particle. All particles of Fig. 5 are confirmed by particle physics experiments. After the hint that the SM might be correct, particle physicists looked for the effects of the SM particles outside the terrestial environment: in the cosmos and stars. Now, it is accepted that there are hints through dark matter and dark energy that the universe evolved with the effects of the BSM particles. However, these were not among the atomists' view in the classical Greek period. Dark matter particles and sterile neutrinos are the BSM particles. In Fig. 5, massless particles are in the grey, which include photon and eight gluons. All the other particles are massive due to the Higgs mechanism. The force mediators are on the second annulus: gluons for the strong interaction, photon for the electromagnetic interaction, and $W^{\pm}$ and $Z$ for the weak interaction. The so-called matter particles, the Greeks' dream, are on the outer annulus. The strongly interacting quarks come in three colours to act as charges of the gluonic force. Weakly interacting particles, not participating in the strong interaction, are leptons, which are shown as white. Here, helicities are denoted by a triangle for L-handed and a bullet for R-handed. Quarks and leptons possessing the same gauge force interactions repeat three times, for which we say, "There are three families in Nature." At the centre, we placed the BEHGHK boson, simply called the Higgs boson whose mass is 125 GeV. Before considering "spontaneous symmetry breaking", the complex Higgs doublet includes four real fields. After "spontaneous symmetry breaking", among these four, three becomes the longitudinal degrees of $W^{\pm}$ and $Z$ in the second annulus and the remaining real field is the 125 GeV Higgs boson. The BEHGHK mechanism is technically realised by assigning a vacuum expectation value (VEV) to one complex component of the doublet, say with the value $V_{\rm EW}$. In one scheme, we have the SM scale where VEV is $V_{\rm EW} = 246\,{\rm GeV}$.

Without many new fundamental discoveries between 1990 and 2012, theorists were free to think about BSM physics without much to worry about. During this period, observations into the sky revealed the need to understand dark matter (DM) and dark energy (DE) as much as atoms. Since the SM particles of Fig. 5 are short of explaining both DM and DE, one has to consider the BSM particles. When we consider these cosmologically hinted phenomena, the classical theory on gravitation must be considered as well. The minimal requirement is to study gravity only with the Einstein equation for gravitation. Regarding DE, Mordehai Milgrom (1946–) introduced an acceleration parameter $a$ in gravity, $a \ll a_0 \sim 10^{-10}\,{\rm m/s^2}$, by naming it Modified Newtonian Dynamics (MOND), which was boosted by Jacob Bekenstein (1947–) (who is famous for suggesting the area rule for the black hole entropy). This acceleration parameter $a$ allows for the distance dependence of gravitation force to deviate from the inverse square rule and gives the observed gravitational effects correctly for the nearby galaxies, but gives a difference for the Type-1 supernovae from which DE was suggested due to their acceleration.

The final words of this chapter are on the BSM-related theories: grand unified theories (GUTs), supersymmetry, supergravity, superstring, DM, DE, WIMPs, "invisible" axions, inflation, and extra dimensions.

"Why is the SM scale so small compared to the Planck mass, $2.43 \times 10^{18}$ GeV"[8] is the so-called *gauge hierarchy problem* in the SM. For fermions such as quarks and leptons, their masses can be neglected at the Planck mass if the L-helicity and R-helicity do not match properly. "Properly" means by considering all symmetries under consideration. The symmetry present in Fig. 5 is the SM gauge symmetry $SU(3) \times SU(2) \times SU(1)$. For example, neutrinos in Fig. 5 arise only with L-handed helicity, which means that neutrino masses can be neglected at the Planck mass scale. It is said that neutrinos are *chiral.* All the other fermions in Fig. 5 are chiral also by considering the SM gauge group. These fermions lose the chiral property if the SM is spontaneously broken by the BEHGHK mechanism. At present, there is no universally accepted solution of the gauge hierarchy problem. Nevertheless, requiring a chiral property in a final theory is very plausible, as emphasised by Howard Georgi in 1979. Basically, this requirement was started since the "V–A" quartet of 1957 : Marshak, Sudarshan, Feynman, and Gell-Mann. When Feynman was asked what was his most important achievement,[9] he replied, "the V–A model".

Counting the number of triangles and bullets in Fig. 5, we have $3\times3$ for whites and $2\times18$ for reds, greens, and yellows, in total 45. It is said that 45 chiral fields are in the SM. Since there are three families, one family contains 15 chiral fields. In 1974, Howard Georgi and Sheldon Glashow grouped these 15 chiral fields into 5 and 10 to arrive at a unifying gauge group SU(5). Because neutrinos are known to be

[8]The Planck mass is basically the inverse of the squarerooted Newton's constant.
[9]R. Leighton and E. Hutchings (eds) *Surely You're Joking, Mr. Feynman!: Adsventures of a Curious Character* (W W Norton, New York, 1985), ISBN 0-393-01921-7.

massive, sometimes it is useful to introduce R-handed counterparts of neutrinos. In this case, one family can be considered in terms of 16 chiral fields. With 16 chiral fields, a unifying gauge group SO(10) was considered by Howard Georgi, and also by Harald Fritzsch and Peter Minkowski in 1974–1975. Quarks and leptons are grouped with the same group property in these SU(5) and SO(10) groups. Hence, SU(5) and SO(10) were considered to be a true unification, and so they are called grand unification groups (GUTs). Still earlier in 1973, Jogesh Pati (1937–) and Abdus Salam (1926–1996) treated quarks and leptons in the same way, but the resulting group was not as simple as SU(5) and it is also called a GUT. Since quarks and leptons are treated in the same way as GUTs, it is possible to transform a proton made of three quarks to a lepton, i.e. a proton can be unstable in GUTs. Discovery of proton decay, though, is not convincing evidence of GUTs because it is possible to make a proton decay without a GUT, for example in an extension of the SM by supersymmetry.

As noticed above in relation to massless fermionic particles, viz., Fig. 5, the chirality concept is natural when we consider very small masses at the Planck mass scale or at the GUT scale. The well-known idea cited by people but not working within this program was the Kaluza–Klein (KK) idea on the electron mass. Naturally, the electron mass in the KK idea was at the Planck scale. This was corrected by Edward Witten in the second Shelter Island Conference in 1983. It was not worthwhile to spend time on unrealisable things, and the modern atomists moved to string theories.

The chirality concept works for the fermions of Fig. 5. In this regard, we note that the Higgs mechanism so far talked about is nothing but the method providing the longitudinal degrees of $W^{\pm}$ and $Z$ gauge bosons. Only, Steven Weinberg wrote a chiral fermion in his paper titled "Model of Leptons" by assigning L-handed electron neutrino and L-handed electron in a doublet toward the CC, thus realising the L-handed CCs envisioned by the "V–A" quartet of 1957. Even if the fermions in the SM can be light, the scale of the Higgs boson is not explained in this way. To understand the ratio (246 GeV)/(Planck mass $= 2.43 \times 10^{18}$ GeV), which is almost $10^{-16}$, an idea similar to the chirality of fermions might be helpful. If it works, the Higgs boson mass can be very small compared to the Planck mass. Still, at what scale the Higgs boson mass is determined is another problem.

Supersymmetry helps assigning boson "a kind of chirality". For chirality, a linear realisation supersymmetry is relating bosons with chiral fermions. Namely, a supersymmetry transformation changes a boson to a fermion and vice versa. This interesting idea was pursued by German physicist Julius Wess (1934–2007) and Italian physicist Bruno Zumino (1923–2014) in 1974. An earlier so-called nonlinear realisation of supersymmetry can be found in the 1971 International Seminar at the Lebedev Institute of Physics in Moscow in Dmitry Volkov's (1925–2015) talk on a new construction generalising the concept of the spontaneously broken internal symmetry groups to the case of groups of a new type including the Poincare group as a subgroup. This work was done with his student A. P. Akulov. But, Volkov and Akulov's neutrino in the title of the paper does not have a bosonic counterpart. So, Wess and Zumino's linear supersymmetry helps in assigning a bosonic chirality.

In the one-to-one matching of bosons and fermions, called $N = 1$ supersymmetry, there is one boson corresponding to a Weyl fermion. Since a Weyl fermion has two components, the corresponding boson has also two components or one complex scalar. With supersymmetry, the 45 chiral fields in Fig. 5 accompany 45 complex scalars. Except the difference in spin, these bosons have the same quantum numbers as their fermionic counterparts. In particular, the chirality quantum numbers of the bosons are the same. The counterpart of the L-handed electron, called L-handed selectron (meaning scalar-electron), carries the L-handedness chirality. Therefore, the L-handed selectron remains light unless the chirality is broken.

Since the hierarchy is so huge, being of order $10^{32}$, making boson light must be true when higher-order terms in quantum field theory are taken into account. Higher-order effects can be calculated by considering all possible Feynman diagrams with the same physical effects. Here, supersymmetry helps. In Fig. 6, we draw an idea on Feynman diagrams. In the discussion on the neutrino oscillation

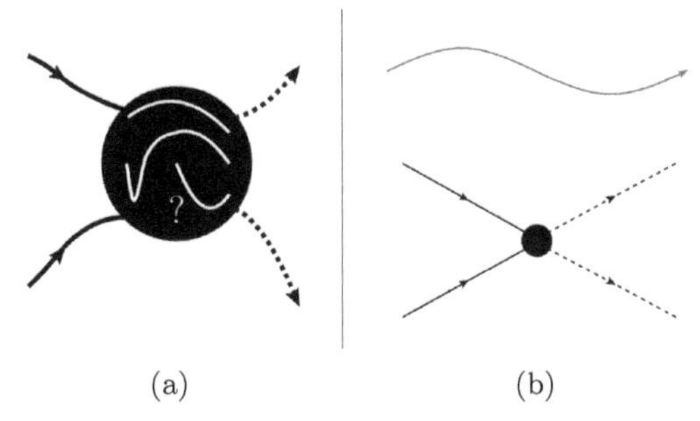


Figure 6: Some ideas on Feynman diagrams. (a) Scattering by two solid line particles into two dashed line particles. (b) If the momenta are small corresponding to large wave length (in red), the scattering does not see the detail interior of a particle.

earlier, we commented that a relevant wave length is important. The wave length specifies the scale below which we do not question what really happens. In Fig. 6(a), the details inside the black ball are not recorded experimentally; look for the outside hints as far as the external observables are the same (two solid lines plus two dashed lines outside the ball). In Fig. 6(b), we show that the detailed structure cannot bc seen with a large wavelength probe shown as a red curve, but quantum field theory provides a method to calculate in detail what is happening inside even though one cannot detect the inside phenomena.

In the hierarchy problem, the Higgs boson mass is in question. Let us denote the Higgs boson mass in Fig. 7 with two outside dashed lines. Here, we showed what is happening for the Higgs boson mass at the one-loop level when the $N = 1$ supersymmetry is effective. When a fermion loop (the solid circle) contributes to the Higgs boson mass, its contribution is negative just because of the fermionic property of the antisymmetric contribution in Fig. 5 of Chapter 5. On the contrary, if a bosonic loop (the dashed circle) contributes to the Higgs boson mass, its contribution is positive because of the bosonic property of the symmetric contribution in Fig. 5 of Chapter 5. With the $N = 1$ supersymmetry, the magnitudes of these contributions are exactly the same. This means that the square of the coupling to the fermion is exactly the same as the boson coupling in the figure on

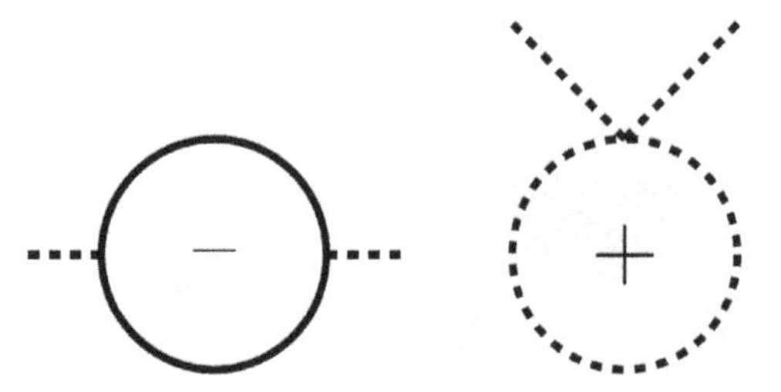


Figure 7: Details contributing to the mass of the Higgs boson with $N = 1$ supersymmetry.

the right-hand side of Fig. 7. The $N = 1$ supersymmetry provides a rationale for this equality. This is the supersymmetry argument to leave the Higgs boson massless at the Planck scale. The basic idea was assigning chirality to the Higgs boson.

The next problem is how to generate the scale 246-GeV VEV of the Higgs doublet in the above supersymmetrised version. Here, one needs help from the gravitational interaction. Gravity extended with supersymmetry is called supergravity. Newton's constant for gravity $G_{\rm Newton}$ is $6.67 \times 10^{-11}\,{\rm N \cdot m^2/kg^2}$ in the MKS units. Particle physicists often use the natural unit, $1/\sqrt{8\pi G_{\rm Newton}}$, which is called the Planck mass, $M_P = 2.43 \times 10^{18}$ GeV. So, gravitational interaction for energies of light particle introduces a ratio (Energy)$/M_P$. In this case, if we have some energy at the so-called intermediate scale, say at $5 \times 10^{10}$ GeV, then the gravitational interaction induces a scale $(5 \times 10^{10}\,{\rm GeV})^2/2.43 \times 10^{18}$ GeV which is roughly 1,000 GeV. This can be used for breaking the electroweak symmetry. This road has been extensively pursued as a supersymmetric extension of the SM by many physicists. For the source of the intermediate scale, a mimic of the quark condensation for the chiral symmetry breaking in QCD has been adopted. It is the condensation of the supersymmetric partner of another strong force, which is usually called a confining gauge group in the hidden sector. Here, "hidden" means that this additional confining force does not interact with the SM particles. But, as of 2019, any expected supersymmetry partner of the SM particles listed in Fig. 5 has not been found at the highest energy accelerator LHC of CERN. "Now is the winter of our discontent," lamented Shakespeare.

Fundamental particles so far explained are point-like particles with the observable sizes given by the (Compton) wavelengths. Can the fundamental particles have shapes as Plato's solids of Fig. 4 of Chapter 1? Maybe strings. Strings were initially studied as the binding force of strongly interacting quarks under the name "dual resonance models" for which the first author reviewed in 1974 the work during 1968–1974,[10] which went out of print in 1979, but was reprinted in 1986 by the World Scientific Publishing Company[11] and promptly sold three times as many copies as the original because of the new interest in superstrings.

With the discovery of the asymptotic freedom, however, QCD was accepted as the correct strong interaction dynamics and, at least for the strong interactions, dual resonance models were forgotten.

Meanwhile, it was known that the allowed extended shapes can be only strings in 10-dimensional space–time. There is one more condition: Strings in 10 dimensions should obey supersymmetry. In 1972, 10-dimensional superstrings were noted by Pierre Ramond (1943–), André Neveu (1946–), and John Schwarz (1941–). In 1974, Joël Scherk (1946–1980) and Schwarz advocated superstring theory for the source of gravity since string theory contained a massless spin-2 particle. This structure superstring must look like a point particle at the wavelengths employed in terrestrial experiments. Thus, superstring theories in 10 dimensions might be a possible extension of the SM at length scales shorter than the electroweak scale $10^{-16}$ cm. Ten years later in 1984, the real development of superstring theory bloomed when all the consistencies of 10-dimensional superstrings were proven, especially in the so-called heterotic string with the gauge group $E_8 \times E_8'$. This group immediately attracted a great deal of attention because branching of $E_8$ leads to a spinor representation in the GUT group SO(10) and the second $E_8'$ can be associated with the hidden sector needed for supersymmetry breaking. The spinor

[10]P. H. Frampton, *Dual Resonance Models* (W. A. Benjamin, Reading, MA, 1974).

[11]P. H. Frampton, *Dual Resonance Models and Superstrings* (World Scientific Publishing Co., Singapore, 1986).

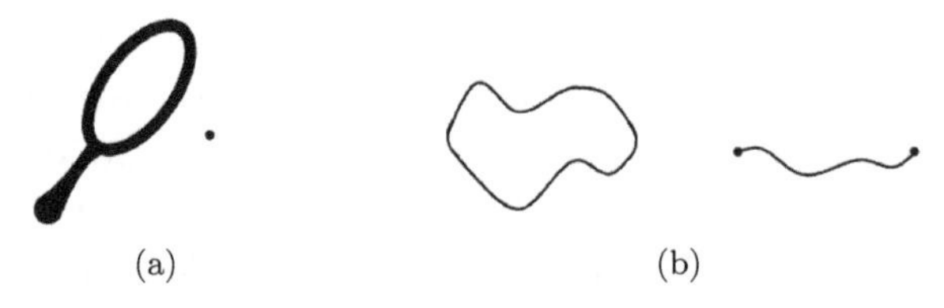


Figure 8: An extended object string: (a) a closed loop and (b) an open string.

representation of SO(10) is signalling a chiral representation as commented before in relation to GUTs.

The first obvious question one can ask is, "How large can a string be?" A natural answer will be its size is somewhat larger than the Planck length, probably around $10^{-31 \text{ to } -32}$ cm. Then, if we look at the point-like particle with a lens of magnifying power $10^{16}$, as depicted in Fig. 8(a), it may look like Fig. 8(b). The heterotic string contains only closed strings whose dimensions are supposedly less than $10^{-30}$ cm and there are string theories including open strings. Note that the Higgs boson Compton wavelength is about $10^{-15}$ cm. Another extreme case is to just allow the string length as large as possible but within the experimental limits from the search for long-range forces via the Cavendish-type experiments. Nima Arkani-Hamed (1972–), Gia Dvali (1964–), and Savas Dimpopoulos (1952–) initiated this kind of large-scale string theories of size 1 mm.

But, the above superstring is given in 10 space–time dimensions. We, living in the four space–time dimensions, must obtain a proper way of obtaining the SM from the 10-dimensional heterotic string. The process is called compactification, hiding six dimensions in 10 looking like internal dimensions to us. Work on the internal six dimensions suggested that they be of the Calabi–Yau shape, as initiated in 1985.

The idea of compactification is most easily understood by compactifying two real dimensions to one real dimension. Consider a sheet of A4 print paper which is a two-dimensional sheet. Then, roll it into a cigar shape. Making the radius of the cigar smaller, it behaves like a thick line becoming a thinner line. Effectively, we obtain one dimension if the wavelength of a probing eye is much larger than the cigar radius. A figure without the imaginery parts of the three

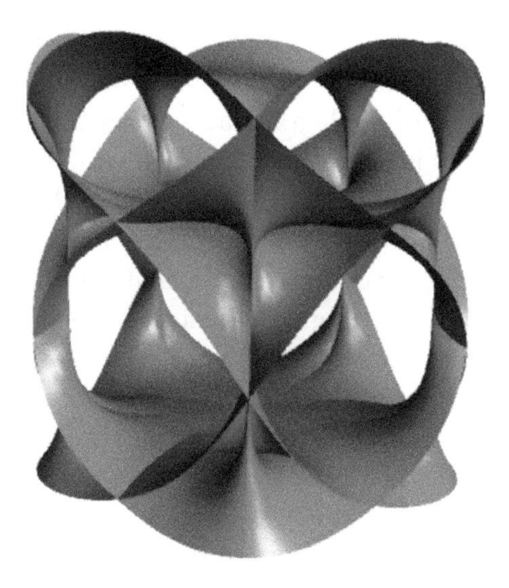

Figure 9: A Calabi–Yau space.

complex Calabi–Yau is shown in Fig. 9. Generalising this idea of compactifying six dimensions, we obtain a four-dimensional theory. It must be supersymmetric since we started from superstring. So, if string is the mother of all fundamental particles, then supersymmetry must show up at some level, but we must wait.

It is hoped that the SM is obtained from some ultraviolet completed theory. For a consistent framework including gravity, therefore, derivation of the SM has been tried in the last three decades, including by the second author, from string theory because only string theory advocates calculable gravitational interactions. To the modern atomists, this attempt is not enough. The compactification should give all the parameters of the SM correctly. Even though some specific routes to the SM in the compactification are assumed, it belongs to a kind of God's design since a definite route to the SM is taken.

Einstein's gravity is said to be "metric" theory, which means that the equation for the metric tensor $g_{\mu\nu}$ is Einstein's gravity. In quantum mechanics, the action defined by the unit of the Planck constant $\hbar$ is the key to understand how important the quantum effects are. The action is an integration of lagrangian (mentioned in the end of Chapter 4), $L(t)$ = (kineticenergy)–(potential energy), with respect to time. More symmetrically, one defines $L(t)$ as the space integral ($\int d^3\mathbf{x}$) of the lagrangian $\mathcal{L}(x)$ at the space–time point $x$. Thus, the action is the space–time integral of the lagrangian ($\int d^4x\mathcal{L}$). Einstein and David Hilbert (1862 AD–1943 AD) noted that the space–time integral of $\mathcal{L}$ multiplied with the squareroot of the determinant of $g_{\mu\nu}$ gives Einstein's gravity equation. In addition, if $\mathcal{L}$ contains a constant, it gives Einstein's cosmological constant (CC), which Einstein introduced after a year of his first theory on the metric theory of gravity of 1916. If the gravitational interaction is given at such a small scale as $10^{-33}$ cm, the first guess on the cosmological constant is $(10^{+33})^4\,\mathrm{cm}^{-4}$, but the observed value is $10^{-120}$ times smaller than that. This is the most severe problem, the cosmological constant problem, among hierarchies on the ratios appearing in physical theories. In compactifications, the CC is also calculated.

In 1998, astrophysical experiments confirmed that the universe is accelerating, with the CC of the order $(0.001\,\mathrm{eV})^4$. The above constant $(10^{+33})^4\,\mathrm{cm}^{-4}$ is about $10^{+120}$ times larger than this value. The number of compactified string models with the CC of this order to be present was estimated as $10^{500}$ by Michael Douglas (1961–). There are so many vacua, but there are some vacua with the CC less than $(0.001\,\mathrm{eV})^4$, which led to the idea of landscape scenario. String compactification allows, as far as the CC is concerned, some universe where our universe might have evolved with such a long history. All the others not belonging to this range of CC are ruled out because they have not lived this long history and humans could not have evolved. This landscape scenario belongs to the anthropic principle which was pointed out by Steve Weinberg and hence belongs to the evolution paradigm.

If quarks were not known, we could not complete the picture of 45 chiral fields in Fig. 5. This was the first moment of peeling the supposed *atoms* after Mendeleev found nuclei. Now, we turn to the story of how quarks in the universe were revealed to us humans.

## Chapter 7

# Order from Chaos

Before discussing mesons and baryons through which the systematisation of the hadrons in the 1960s is derived, we need to describe two transformative papers published, respectively, in 1954 and 1956, both involving Frank (Chen Ning) Yang (1922–). The second paper was briefly discussed in Chapter 6 and will be discussed further at the end of this chapter.

The first paper, with Robert Mills (1927–1999), provided a crucial generalisation of quantum electrodynamics (QED) which had already been established as a completely satisfactory theory of electrons and photons, agreeing with experiment to unprecedented accuracy. Today, the magnetic moment of the muon calculated from QED agrees with experiment to an astonishing one part in 1 trillion, the most accurate theory ever discovered.

The range of the electromagnetic force is practically infinite. If the wavelength is long enough, as in most cases (red colour in Fig. 6(b) of Chapter 6), one wavelength sweeps the whole region of the bullet in Fig. 6(b) of Chapter 6. There are two more fundamental forces which are effectively short-range forces compared to the electromagnetic force. Beyond electrodynamics, leptons and hadrons experience these short-range interactions which are strong and weak interactions. In the nucleus, these strong and weak forces are working only inside nuclei, i.e. in the black bullet in Fig. 6(b) if the bullet is identified as a nucleus. For the leptons, the strong force does not apply and the range of the weak force is similar to that in hadrons.

This is a reason that weak force is sometimes called "weak nuclear force". The story of weak force or weak interactions is the topic of Chapter 8.

The strong interactions hold together the atomic nucleus, overriding the electric repulsion between the positively charged protons. Since the strong force is restricted to the inside of the nucleus, it is a very short-range force. The reason it is short range (quark confinement) is completely different from that of the weak force. Now, the question is, "How can QED be generalised to accommodate this strong force?"

The key symmetry which underlies the success and uniqueness of QED is local gauge invariance. The force mediator in QED is the photon: gauge boson accompanied with the gauge principle. Pions were supposed to be the mediators for the strong force holding the atomic nuclei together, but they are not particles implied by some gauge principle. Before introducing the U(1) gauge principle for the photon, one considers the conservation of electromagnetic charge.

The charge conservation in quantum mechanics is the phase symmetry discussed in Chapter 5: $\Psi \to e^{ie\theta}\Psi$ ($e$ is the charge of electron) such that the observable probability $\Psi^*\Psi$ is invariant under this phase transformation. Invariance under this phase transformation is called "global" U(1) symmetry. It is "global" because $\theta$ is the same for any space–time points in the universe. QED involves making the phase depend on position $x$: $\Psi \to e^{iq\theta(x)}\Psi$, where $q$ is the electric charge and parameter $\theta(x)$ (or sometimes the whole factor $e^{iq\theta(x)}$) is the phase. Being the offspring of quantum mechanics, it is a unitary transformation. And, there is only one $x$-dependent parameter $\theta(x)$ by which we call it U(1) gauge theory, where we have interchangeable words (gauge) = (local). In QM dealing with electrons, the charge was the electromagnetic charge $q = -e$.

In Fig. 1(a), we show a global rotation. "Global" means that the same number is taken over all space. If we consider an electron orbiting around a proton (to this kind of electron, the atom is its whole universe), the electron wave function is depicted as the cloud in Fig. 1(a), which can be denoted as $\Psi(\mathbf{x})$. The phase symmetry mentioned above is that rotation $e^{ie\theta}$ is the same at any point $\mathbf{x}$.

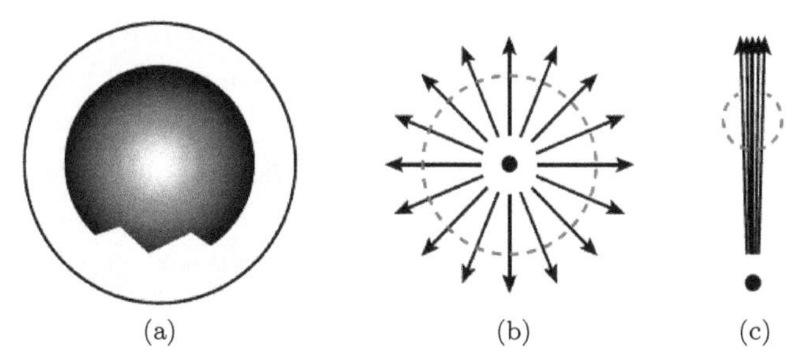


Figure 1: U(1)'s: (a) A global rotation. (b) Gauge fields (**E**) from a charge $q$, where the red dashline depicts a Gaussian surface enclosing the charge. (c) Collecting **E** field lines of (b) into one direction. Here, the dashed circle is going around the collected flux lines of field.

For $Ne$ charge, then how can one calculate the global number? We enclose the source by a large closing bag, most conveniently a surface of a large sphere, the Gaussian surface, denoted as a yellow sphere in Fig. 1(a). Then, count all charges in this Gaussian surface. This is the way to count the global charges.[1] The phase rotation is for the whole wave function inside this yellow surface, $\Psi \to e^{iNe\,\theta}\Psi$.

For a U(1) "gauge" or "local" symmetry, the differences in the space–time points are usually denoted as a Taylor expansion, which in the continuum limit involves an expansion by $\frac{\partial}{\partial x^\mu}$, denoted conveniently as $\partial_\mu$. If the angle $\theta$ depends on $x$, i.e. $\theta(x)$, the difference in the nearby points involves $\partial_\mu \Psi(x)$. Then, $\partial_\mu(e^{iNe\theta}\Psi)$ has to take account of acting $\partial_\mu$ on $e^{iNe\theta(x)}$. To make this effect unnoticeable, one must have a field compensating this derivative. It is called the gauge field $A_\mu$, having the space–time index as $\partial_\mu$. The photon in QED is introduced in this way.

In QED, how do we calculate the charge inside the Gaussian surface? Since $\theta(x)$ depends on $x$, we cannot calculate as done in Fig. 1(a). But, in the Gaussian surface, there are electric field lines going out from a positive charge as shown in Fig. 1(b). At each point on the Gaussian surface, we know the electric field **E** and we sum up the **E** field flux over the whole closure of the Gaussian surface. That sum is proportional to the total electric charge inside the Gaussian

[1]The lepton and baryon numbers are also counted in this way.

surface. If the surface is not closed, one cannot be sure that one measured the charge correctly. For example, one small hole can take out a significant portion of the flux, as shown in Fig. 1(c).

To render the short-range forces of strong and weak nuclear interactions as local ones, it is better to start with global symmetries as done above for U(1). Strong forces are mediated at the 100 MeV scale by three pions and hence U(1) is not a candidate for strong force. The weak nuclear force is effectively described by charged currents, which can carry positive or negative charge. Here again, therefore, U(1) is not suitable for the weak nuclear force.

In 1932, right after the discovery of neutrons, looking at the two particles, proton $p$ and neutron $n$ in the same way, Werner Heisenberg discovered a useful approximate symmetry. This is due to the fact that there is a very small mass difference 1.3 MeV between neutron $n$ and proton $p$ with their respective masses 939.6 MeV and 938.3 MeV. This was first measured by Chadwick and Goldhaber in 1933. So, the neutron–proton mass difference is just 0.15 % of their average mass and hence Heisenberg considered them as the same in a first approximation. In this case, protons and neutrons behave in the same way as far as strong interaction is concerned, which is represented by the isospin group SU(2). The fundamental representation of SU(2) is two-dimensional, being proton and neutron, which is called a doublet. The doublet can be grouped as $(p, n)$. The generalisation of this, looking at $N$ particles in the same way, is SU($N$), and its fundamental representation is then $N$-plet, $(\psi_1, \psi_2, \ldots, \psi_N)$.

The unitary transformation is the rule of transformation in quantum mechanics. For an $N$-plet, the transformation is done by the matrix multiplication $\Psi_k \to [e^{iM_{ij}\theta_{ij}}]_{kl}\Psi_l$, where $i, j, k, l$ vary from 1 to $N$. The number in the set $ij$ in the exponent with the unitarity condition being $N^2$ for U($N$), but proper counting for $SU$(N) is to subtract 1 from that (technically an SU($N$)-transformation determinant is 1, adding S for special unitary group); thus, the allowed number of parameters $\theta_{ij}$ in SU(N) is $(N^2 - 1)$.

As we generalised a global U(1) to a local U(1) before, now it looks like a simple matter to generalise a global SU($N$) to a local SU($N$). The idea of Yang and Mills was to consider this kind of more general phase transformation such that parameters $\theta_{ij}(x)$ are consistently introduced when they are made $x$ dependent: $\Psi_k \to [e^{igM_{ij}\theta_{ij}(x)}]_{kl}\Psi_l$, in which $g$ is a gauge coupling constant and $M$ is a square $N \times N$ matrix. These $N \times N$ matrices generally do not commute and satisfy a non-trivial non-commutative algebra. The lagrangian for such a theory, called a Yang–Mills theory or a non-abelian gauge theory, generalises the QED lagrangian by introducing covariant derivatives to replace normal derivatives and a generalisation of the usual kinetic energy term, using the covariant derivatives. It was generally realised that the Yang–Mills idea was very likely to be a key ingredient in a correct theory, although it was several years before the appropriate application was identified. Remarkably, this Yang and Mills paper was never recognised by a Nobel Prize but did lead to at least 20 future Nobel Prizes.

The covariant derivative of the Yang–Mills theory needs a profound ingredient that includes a nonlinear term in the covariant derivative of the SU($N$) gauge fields. This nonlinear term is the source for the asymptotic freedom and instanton solutions.

By 1960, there was a quite chaotic situation with respect to the many hadrons, baryons, and mesons which had shown up in experiments. There was no rhyme or reason until a breakthrough by Murray Gell-Mann in 1961 who realised that isospin, for which the symmetry group is Heisenberg's global SU(2), must be enlarged to a global SU(3) with the additional rank used to accommodate strangeness quantum number $S$, a quantum number introduced by Gell-Mann earlier in 1955, for a subset of the mesons and baryons which did not decay by strong interactions.

As explained in Fig. 1(a), any global quantum number of U(1) for a wave function, or in the whole universe, can be measured. This is just for one quantum number. Heisenberg's SU(2) considers only one diagonal quantum number in SU(2) even though it is a non-abelian global group. The number of diagonalisable quantum numbers is called the rank of the group in consideration. Diagonalisable ones are said to be commuting, and form what is technically called the Cartan subalgebra with dimension equal to the rank of the original group. If non-diagonalisable matrices are included, it produces "non-commuting" algebra. So, a non-abelian gauge group has a non-commuting algebra: non-abelian means non-commuting and abelian means commuting. If we consider two quantum numbers, we should consider $\mathrm{U}(1) \times \mathrm{U}(1)$. These two U(1)'s commute. But, combining with Heisenberg's SU(2), we consider a rank 2 group $\mathrm{SU}(2) \times \mathrm{U}(1)_\mathrm{S}$, where $\mathrm{U}(1)_\mathrm{S}$ denotes the group of transformation with the strangeness quantum number $S$.

Gell-Mann's legacy starts by making the whole group $\mathrm{SU}(2) \times \mathrm{U}(1)_\mathrm{S}$ a simple group of rank 2 with isospin SU(2) and strangeness $\mathrm{U}(1)_\mathrm{S}$. Rank 2 simple groups are limited: four classical groups SU(3), SO(4), SO(5), and Sp(4), and one exceptional group $\mathrm{G}_2$. SO(4), SO(5), and Sp(4) are very short of satisfying the accumulated hadron data. Gell-Mann found his eight-fold way in SU(3), and declared that the needed non-abelian rank 2 group is SU(3). Here, we note that the group, including Ben Lee, at the University of Pennsylvania pushed for $\mathrm{G}_2$, but Nature chose the eight-fold way and hence SU(3). Here, we emphasise again that the non-abelian group SU(3) is a global group but not a gauge one. As will be discussed in Chapter 8, in the current understanding of continuous symmetries, spin-0 pseudoscalars can be light due to spontaneous symmetry breaking of the mother global symmetry. If it were a gauge symmetry, we do not talk about spin-0 pseudoscalars but spin-1 gauge bosons. Therefore, to interpret pseudoscalar mesons, the symmetry must be global. But, in the early 1960s, it was not clear to physicists.

In terms of this global SU(3), called flavour SU(3), the mesons fall into singlet and octet irreducible representations. Indeed, there is one octet of pseudoscalars including the $\pi$ and $K$ mesons, and a second octet of vectors including $\rho$ and $K^*$ mesons, as shown in Fig. 2. The baryons are in octets and decuplets of SU(3). All mesons and baryons in a given irreducible representation have a common spin and parity, denoted as $J^P$. Observation of this regularity by Gell-Mann was remarkable. It was the first since the periodicity of chemical elements was found by Dmitri Mendeleev in 1859. In Gell-Mann's SU(3), it is more intuitive to draw pictures in the plane rather than presenting with tables. Because its rank is two, i.e. two diagonalisable quantum numbers, usually the $x$ coordinate is used for the third component of

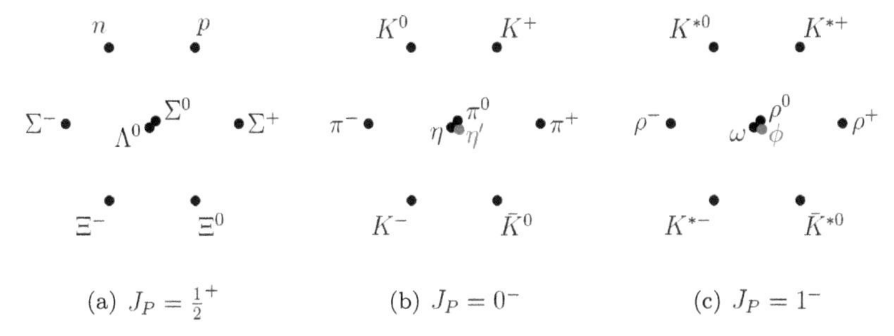


Figure 2: The eight-fold way: (a) Baryons, (b) pseudoscalar mesons, and (c) vector mesons.

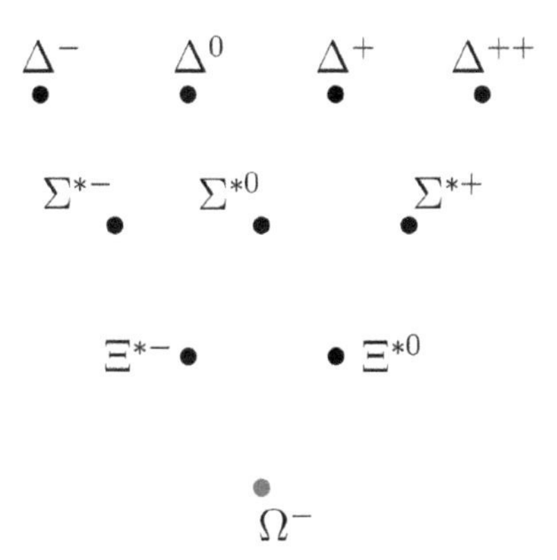


Figure 3: The decuplet $J^P = \frac{3}{2}^+$.

isospin and the $y$ coordinate is strangeness $S$. Shifting the strangeness by the baryon number, sometimes "hypercharge" $Y \equiv (S + B)$ is instead used as the $y$ coordinate. The baryon octet for $J_P = \frac{1}{2}^+$ is shown in Fig. 2(a), and meson octets for $J_P = 0^-$ and $J_P = 1^-$ are shown in Figs. 2(b) and 2(c) as black bullets.

There are spin-$\frac{3}{2}$ baryons which are shown in a decuplet of $J^P = \frac{3}{2}^+$ in Fig. 3. When the spin-$\frac{3}{2}$ baryons were studied in 1962, both Gell-Mann and Susumu Okubo (1930–2015) found that one component was missing. It was $\Omega^-$ with $J^P = \frac{3}{2}^+$, Mass $=$ 1,680 MeV, and strangeness $S = -3$. In particular, Gell-Mann made a very specific prediction that $\Omega^-$ particle decays principally by the mode $\Omega^- \to \Lambda^0 + K^-$ and $\Xi^0 + \pi^-$.

In an experiment at BNL by Nicolas Samios (1932–) and collaborators, the $\Omega^-$ with all the predicted properties was discovered, sealing the fame of Gell-Mann and the validity of the SU(3) classification, which he called the "Eight-fold way". Thus, a chaotic situation was brought to order as the first real triumph of particle theory.

The success of SU(3) flavour symmetry led to the consideration by Gell-Mann in 1964 of the fundamental representation of SU(3), which is a triplet out of which all the hadrons might be made. We noted earlier in Chapter 6 that the fundamental representation of SU(3) was also considered by Shoichi Sakata in 1957, but the octet of baryons cannot be made in this way. Taking three quarks (as Gell-Mann called the hadron constituents, based on James Joyce's *Finnegan's Wake*) $u, d, s$, then the proton is $(uud)$, the neutron is $(udd)$, and the $\Omega^-$ is $(sss)$. George Zweig (1937–) independently considered the same constituents, but with the name Aces. At first, this was presented as merely a mathematical shorthand, but as time progressed to the late 1960s, it became clear that the the quarks are physical and real point-like constituents of hadrons.

Given that quarks are spin-$\frac{1}{2}$ fermions, one can extend SU(3) together with spin to SU(6) global symmetry from which $J = \frac{1}{2}^+$ baryon octet and $J = \frac{3}{2}^+$ baryon decuplet are combined together. These constitute 56 entries $(8 \times 2 + 10 \times 4)$ in a single representation and SU(6) tells "Aha, **56** is completely symmetric under exchange of quarks!" More explicitly, for $\Omega^- = (sss)$, if all spins of $s$ are up $s^\uparrow s^\uparrow s^\uparrow$ (which is contained in **56**), then exchange of any pair is symmetric. But, the quark $s$ is assumed to be fermion and the spin–statistics theorem implied in Fig. 5(a) of Chapter 5 requires total antisymmetry. This was a big hurdle to the quark model and Oscar Greenberg introduced Parastatistics in addition to the established Fermi–Dirac and Bose–Einstein statistics. A solution came from Moo-Young Han (1934–2016) and Yoichiro Nambu (1921–2015) with another non-abelian group which must be SU(3) under the assumption that, as in the eight-fold way, three quarks make up baryons. But, despite introducing additional SU(3) symmetry, it failed in correctly predicting the electromagnetic charges of quarks.

In fact, they intended to introduce integer charge quarks because there was no hint of Gell-Mann's fractional quarks in the universe. The electromagnetic charge is in the electroweak part and hence for strong interactions it does not matter, and we credit them as the first physicists to have introduced the additional SU(3) degree for strong interactions consistently with the spin–statistics theorem. The correct electric charges agreeing with Gell-Mann's original charge assignment was discovered by Gell-Mann with Harald Fritzsch (1943–) in 1972, and a Yang–Mills theory for strong interactions using this SU(3) was put forward. This is called quantum chromodynamics (QCD). This is a different SU(3) from the eight-fold way, and acts not on flavour but on a new quantum number named colour. Each quark flavour comes in three colours called red, green, and yellow. QCD is now universally accepted as the correct theory of strong interactions, at least at accessible energies.

So far, we have discussed the strong force and its role to confine quarks within nuclear size, and in consequence the regularities appearing in the resultant hadrons. There are three fundamental issues here. One is how the strong force sticks the quarks together, and the second is seeing them by short wavelength probes. Finally, as for propagation of electromagnetic waves which are solutions of the QED field equations, can there be meaningful solutions of QCD field equations?

Regarding the second issue, at the very-short-distance scales probed by the high energy (at that time) electron beam of (=Stanford Linear Accelerator Center SLAC), Democritus' idea was revived in the quark-parton model where the elementary quarks become evident in deep inelastic scattering as suggested by James Bjorken (1934–). In an article with Emmanuel Paschos (1944–), Bjorken pointed out that if you wish to see what is within the proton, you shine intense light to it. The scaling behaviour observed in high-energy electron and neutrino scattering experiments on nuclear targets completely agrees with the quark-parton model with nucleus containing three valence quarks. This success was possible because QCD behaves as if it interacts weakly at small separations, a property called asymptotic freedom. Asymptotic freedom was found by Harvard physicist David

Politzer (1949–), and Princeton physicists David Gross (1941–) and Frank Wilczek (1951–). In addition, there are sea quarks and gluons. So, inside the proton, three valence quarks ($uud$) and "sea" quarks $(u\bar{u}), (d\bar{d}), (s\bar{s}), (c\bar{c}), \ldots,$ and gluons jiggle around. The quarks and gluons are indeed real physical particles.

Regarding the first issue, the asymptotic freedom guarantees that the QCD coupling constant becomes very strong at low-energy scale (at long-distance separations), providing an explanation for quark confinement and chiral symmetry breaking, not yet proven rigorously. Quark confinement is a simple word for why quarks are permanently confined inside hadrons and cannot be produced singly. The number of parameters of transformation under colour SU(3) is $3^2 - 1$ as mentioned earlier and there are eight gluons. Because QCD is not broken, we listed gluons in Fig. 5 of Chapter 6 as massless particles. As mentioned earlier, even if gluons are massless, the strong force is short range due to the quark confinement or more generally confinement of all coloured particles, both quarks and gluons.

Regarding the third issue, let us refer to Fig. 1(b). In three space dimensions, the surface of the sphere denoted as the dashed curve is a balloon enclosing the sphere. The balloon is called a two-dimensional sphere denoted as $S_2$. In four space–time dimensions, Fig. 1(b) is a world line. World lines denote particle trajectories, and Fig. 1(b) in the world line is a trajectory of a charged particle.

Can we consider a surface enclosing a four-dimensional sphere? For this purpose, consider a four-dimensional Euclidian space $E_4$. But, we cannot take a picture of a four-dimensional object. So, imagine Fig. 4(a) as just a four-dimensional sphere. Its surface is a three-dimensional sphere, which is denoted as $S_3$. A point (or a sphere in our case) in four dimensions is similar to hamiltonian or lagrangian because earlier we noted that action is $\int d^4x\mathcal{L}$.

Can we assign $\mathbf{E}$ or $\mathbf{B}$ fields on the surface $S_3$ of Fig. 4(a)? To have a perfect match on the position in $S_3$ of Fig. 4(a), the gauge fields must have the same geometrical property in the internal group space. Because $S_3$ is three-dimensional, we need three directions in the internal space. It is done with SU(2) internal space. We have repeatedly commented that the parameters in the unitary

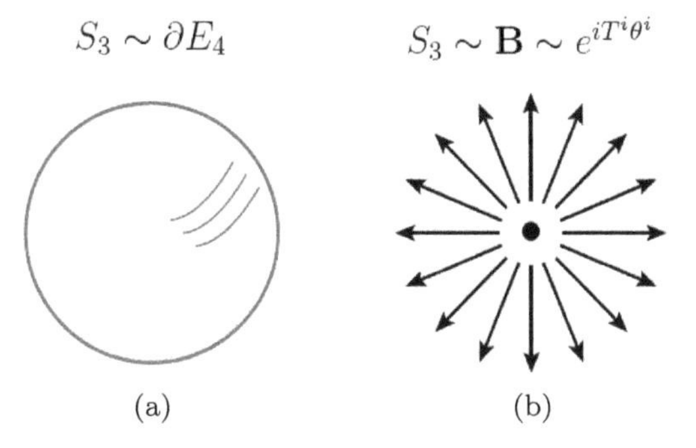


Figure 4: Instanton.

transformation are phases, which means that they are sitting on the surface of spheres of radius 1. SU(2) has three parameters and hence describes $S_3$ on the surface of unit radius. Thus, SU(2) gauge field strengths can sit on the $S_3$ of Fig. 4(a). These solutions, Fig. 4(b), are instanton solutions. "Instanton" is because they occur at one point (Fig. 4(a)) or instant in four-dimensional space–time. Since SU(2) is a subgroup of colour SU(3), the physics discussed with the instanton solution is applicable to QCD and to all non-abelian gauge groups. An explicit instanton solution was presented by USSR physicists Alexander Belavin (1942–), Alexander Polyakov (1945–), Albert Schwartz (1934–), and Yu. S. Tyupkin. This instanton solution was the beginning of finding out another parameter $\Theta$ in QCD, unknown before the discovery of the instanton solution.

In Fig. 4, the size of the ball appears necessarily. Since the nonlinear term of the gauge fields is the source of the instanton solution, this size is roughly the scale where this non-abelian gauge group becomes strong where the contribution is said to be O(1). If the instanton size is relatively smaller, then the effect of the instanton solution is exponentially suppressed compared to the O(1) contribution. For QCD instantons, this O(1) appears around several hundred MeV. If QCD becomes strong at a very-high-energy scale, due to the presence of many particles above the TeV scale, then one can consider correspondingly small scale instantons. But, there is no need to consider these extremely small instantons.

If non-zero $\Theta$ is present, QCD has a source of CP violation. QCD interactions do not violate the flavour symmetry, and hence the CP violation effects by strong interaction can be seen only by electric dipole moments. For the proton, its electric charge makes the dipole moment unobservably small even if it is present. So, the static property of neutron is the best test ground for the electric dipole moment. The current bound on the neutron electric dipole moment is about $10^{-26}e$cm, restricting the bound on QCD's $|\Theta|$ to about $10^{-12}$ because the size of the neutron is about $10^{-14}$ cm. The QCD parameter $|\Theta|$, intrinsically present, must be very small, which is a new type of hierarchy problem. In QCD, this is called the Strong CP Problem.

So far, we looked into the supposedly elementay particle proton and found out that there are more fundamental particles inside it: gluons and quarks. Without quarks, we are far away from filling out the particles of Fig. 5 of Chapter 6. This story invites us to make quarks and leptons composites of even more fundamental fermions under the name of urs and prions. But, such attempts have not been successful so far.

Gauge symmetries are the favoured symmetries in particle physics. One reason is depicted in Fig. 5, where the same angle is rotated on the Earth and on the Moon. The information of rotation on the Earth by angle $\theta$ to go to the Moon takes about 1.3 seconds at the speed of light and the simultaneous rotation at both places by the same angle $\theta$ is logically not allowed. But, if rotations depend on the position $x$, there is no need for $\theta$ (Moon) to be the same as $\theta$ (Earth). Thus, local symmetry is preferred by particle physicists.

In the standard model (SM) of particle physics, local symmetries are used for the elementary particle forces. Just counting the numbers, U(1) gauge symmetry is used for electromagnetism, SU(2) gauge symmetry is used for the weak interactions, and SU(3) gauge symmetry (which we called colour above) is used for strong interactions. Thus, the SM is gauge theory based on the gauge group $SU(3) \times SU(2) \times U(1)$. The colour gauge symmetry $SU(3)_{colour}$ is unbroken, but there is the important unsolved problem in

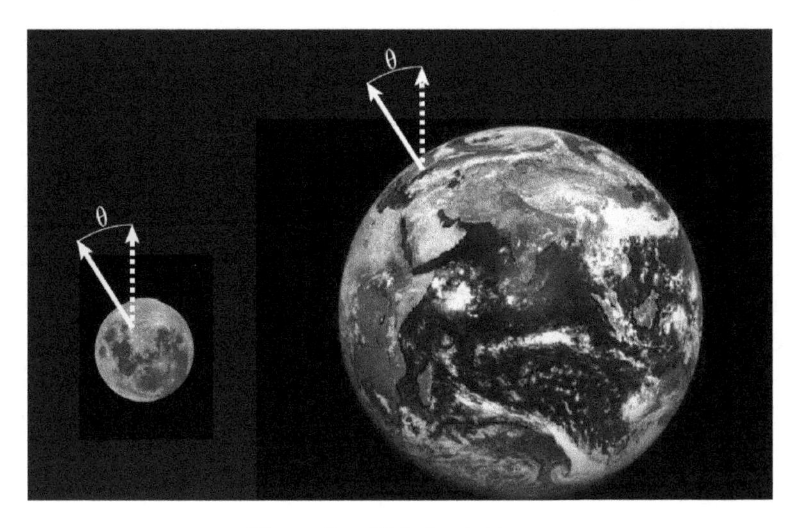


Figure 5: Global rotations.

$SU(3)_{colour}$: the confinement mechanism of colour. Now, we turn to the story of the electroweak gauge group $SU(2) \times U(1)$.

Both of the Yang papers introduced at the beginning of this chapter played central roles in the discovery of the standard model. Parity violation is crucial because it necessitates using chiral fermions in the theory, which will be exploited in more detail in Chapter 8. This leads to constraints arising from the cancellations of quantum anomalies which would be automatically absent were parity to be respected.

Parity-symmetric nature, changing coordinate $\mathbf{x}$ to $-\mathbf{x}$, was the God-given belief in the early days of quantum mechanics until 1956. In 1924, Otto Laporte (1902–1971) proposed that atomic wave functions are either symmetric or antisymmetric. Soon in 1927, Eugene Wigner (1902–1995) concluded that the Laporte rule was an aspect of parity-symmetric nature. As we know now, electrodynamics, the leading force working in the world of atoms, does conserve parity symmetry. Wolfgang Pauli was greatly influential in making particle physicists believe strongly in parity conservation. In atomic physics, it was very difficult to get any hint of parity violation. Even after the standard model was known, detection of parity violation from atomic physics was initially more difficult than in particle physics.

If parity is broken, it must be discovered from weak interactions, especially from decays of relatively long-lived particles. In Chapter 6, we already discussed this from the tau–theta puzzle. After the parity violation idea was mentioned in the ICHEP-6 Rochester conference, Tsung Dao Lee and Chen Ning Yang suggested that one can prove it from weak decay experiments such as $\Lambda$-decay and $^{60}$Co-decay. If we take into account rotations, parity operation is identical to "mirror reflection". In the mirror, left (L) and right (R) are changed. Why? Because you are standing up. So, devise an experiment to have a particle standing up. For this, spin direction is pretty good.

In Fig. 6, the essence of mirror reflection is depicted. Like a person standing up, a spin direction is given on the L-hand side. In the mirror, the spin direction is reversed because it is like the (orbital) angular momentum. The orbit is in the opposite direction in the mirror and the angular momentum direction is reversed. A particle moving with momentum direction $\mathbf{p}$ looks like $\tilde{\mathbf{p}}$ in the mirror. The first confirmation of parity violation in weak decays came from this simple diagram performed by Madame Chien-Shiung Wu (1912–1997) at Columbia University. The nucleus was the radioactive

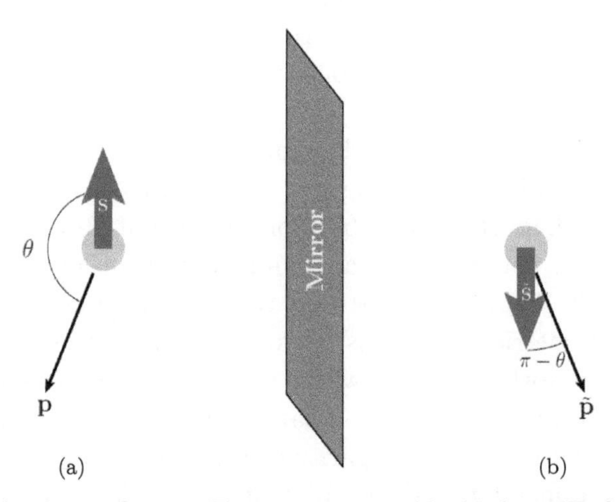


Figure 6: A mirror reflection. This setup was used by Madame Wu for the decay of $^{60}$Co.

isotope $^{60}$Co with half-life 5.3 years. So, in nature it is not present. But, it can be manufactured artificially and has the magnetic moment which was aligned by the external magnetic field by Madame Wu. So, the spin direction is aligned to the upward direction as in Fig. 6(a). Suppose that the decay produces a particle with momentum $\mathbf{p}$ with the angle $\theta$. The mirror reflection of this is shown in Fig. 6(b) going with angle $\pi - \theta$ with the spin direction. So, if nature is parity symmetric, we expect as many events in the southern hemisphere as in the northern hemisphere. What Madame Wu found was that there are more electrons coming in the southern hemisphere than in the northern hemisphere, and that parity is violated in the decay process. Nuclear beta decay is a weak process and it established a maximal parity violation in weak interactions.

## Chapter 8

# Electroweak Unification

In Chapter 6, we listed the dream particles only dreamed of by ancient atomists in Fig. 5 of Chapter 6. In this chapter, we discuss the aspects related to the chiral property of these particles, especially how the weak and electromagnetic forces are unified ("electroweak") in the Standard Model (SM) and in particular (1) how the SM fermions remain light, (2) the mystery of the light Higgs boson mass, and (3) possible unification of the SM into a grand unified theory (GUT) with the chiral property intact.

Weak interaction phenomena, known since Henri Becquerel (1852–1908) accidentally discovered that uranium salts spontaneously emit a penetrating radiation in 1896, have been completely understood in the second half of the 20th century. At length scales larger than $10^{-16}$ cm, the reality of quarks as discussed in Chapter 7 is of prime importance in ordering the jigsaw puzzle of elementary particles into Fig. 5 of Chapter 6. Particle physicists call this established model the SM of particle physics. All the fundamental particles in the SM are given in Fig. 5 of Chapter 6, the heart of atomists' dream since the ancient Greeks. Here, we also include the story that finally established "how they pull or push each other", the so-called *interactions of elementary particles.*

We study the universe and particles in it only after some point where we can reliably calculate the numbers. We are not philosophers, and do not question the creation of the universe as religious priests do. So, we are the evolutionists until the end of this chapter. Only if we can calculate numbers from first principles can we confidently talk about them as scientific knowledge.

Soon after the creation of the universe, the universe's temperature was low enough (compared to GUT scale) such that calculations based on the SM have been possible. The time after the beginning of this expansion era was $10^{-12}$ second. At that time, the universe was extremely hot with the temperature ten thousand trillion degrees Celsius. All the SM particles were moving with light velocity then. As the universe cools, the most massive particles lose the kinetic energy and are almost at rest in the comoving sphere of the universe. In a sense, it is similar to cooling oxtail soup. When one boils oxtail soup, mutton fat get dissolved in water at high temperature, but it get aggregated into white solids when the temperature is lowered. A similar phenomenon occurs for elementary particles, but with the governing laws of particle physics. Below a certain temperature, usually measured by the energy unit of eV (by particle physicists) that is roughly 10,000 Celsius, particles of mass of that temperature cease to move with light velocity. They become annihilated and leave no trace to the observers coming at a later time in the universe. We humans coming in 14 billion years later with the tool box, the SM kit, cannot know how these very heavy particles acted in the beginning of the universe. The question to answer is, "Which particles are here and now?" or, "Which particles are allowed to move with the light velocity at the time of $10^{-12}$ second?" We know what particles are here and now; they are listed in Fig. 5 of Chapter 6. But, to answer the second question, there must be a knowledge of physics applicable at the time $10^{-12}$ second. This problem may be related to the gauge hierarchy problem. The beta decay Becquerel observed had originated due to the so-called charged current (CC) weak interaction.

At this stage, we ask, "Which particles remain moving with light velocity?" In Fig. 1, we show **L** and **R** with thick arrows, denoting the spin angular momentum direction. Let us get an idea of how large the angular momentum will be if it were an orbital angular momentum which is proportional to the product of the rotating arm (horizontal small arrow) and the velocity of the rotating point. If the rotating

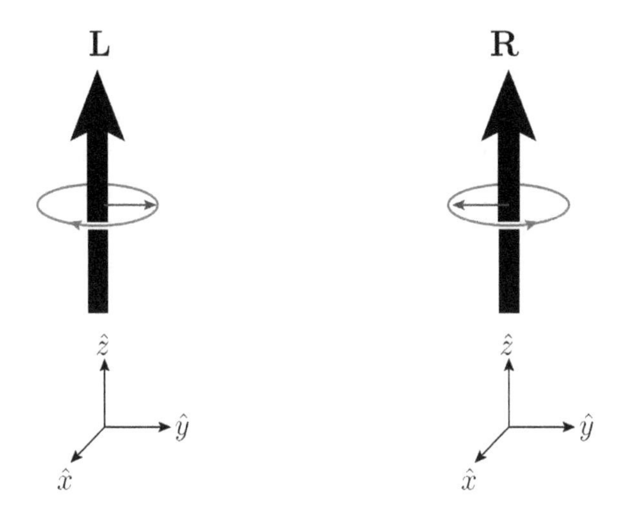


Figure 1: Rotating senses of L and R used in the text.

arm is zero, the orbital angular momentum is zero. If a particle moves with light velocity and has a non-vanishing angular momentum that has three components, two components of angular momentum must be perpendicular to the propagating direction $\hat{z}$, i.e. in the $(xy)$-plane or equivalently **L** or **R**. If one looks at the propagating direction, i.e. from the bottom of Fig. 1, **L** has the counterclockwise rotation (so $-1$ in the right-hand coordinate system) and **R** has the clockwise rotation (so $+1$ in the right-hand coordinate system). We obtain this conclusion because if it has mass, then its velocity must be smaller than the velocity of light and we can change the angular momentum into any direction off the $(xy)$-plane by changing its propagation velocity. But, for particles always moving with light velocity, the only direction is in the perpendicular direction. We name this helicity, from a helical orbital motion when propagating in the $\hat{z}$ direction. Another word we use is polarisation. The best example is light which has two polarisations. Massless particles having angular momentum, for the spin angular momentum, have only two transverse polarisations. In this sense, the spin-2 graviton has two helicities, $+2$ and $-2$.

In 1957, 1 year after the discovery of parity violation in weak interactions, the "V–A" CC weak interaction was suggested by the

"V–A" quartet, Marshak, Sudarshan, Feynman, and Gell-Mann. In the SM, the "V–A" CC weak interaction was suggested by Steven Weinberg by assigning the electron-type neutrino and L-handed electron of Fig. 5 of Chapter 6 in the same way in weak interactions as a doublet $(\nu_{eL}, e_L)$. In Fig. 1, the thick arrows denote this setup, **L** denoting the counterclockwise rotation and **R** denoting the clockwise rotation. $(\nu_e)_L$ and $(e)_L$ in Fig. 5 of Chapter 6 interact with the $W^{\pm}$ boson exactly in the same way. The bullet electron of Fig. 5 of Chapter 6 never interacts with $W^{\pm}$. Realisation of this simple fact was seriously applied in GUTs and extended GUTs by Howard Georgi, proposing the *survival hypothesis* on the masses. It is a hypothesis similar to conjectures if one cannot be certain of choosing one category among various possibilities. There are many ifs on the fundamentals on theories. One obvious one in particle physics like axioms in mathematics is *gauge symmetry*, which was discussed in Chapter 7. If we add many more decorations in addition to gauge symmetry such as discrete symmetries and global symmetries, particle theory can give almost infinite possibilities.

The survival hypothesis proposes that any pair with both L and R with the same gauge charge obtains mass at the temperature in consideration, i.e. at $10^{16}$ degrees Celsius, as mutton fat aggregates at some cold temperature. If there is no matching, then it is massless. Neutrinos with L-handedness only in Fig. 5 of Chapter 6 do not find their R-handed counterparts and remain massless at $10^{16}$ degrees Celsius. For electrons, the L-handed electron finds the R-handed one (bullet symbol), but their gauge charges are different; it is not a perfect matching. So, both L-handed and R-handed electrons remain massless at $10^{16}$ degrees Celsius or at $10^{12}$ eV in terms of energy scale. In this way, the SM particles remain massless even if the temperature is lowered to below $10^{12}$ eV. To reiterate, the first people to suggest this result, even if not spoken in this manner, were the "V–A" quartet of 1957.

When both chiralities $L$ and $R$ have otherwise the same quantum numbers, they combine to form a Dirac mass term at the ambient temperature, i.e. at $10^{16}$ degrees Centigrade. Without such matching, the states remain massless. This is called the "survival hypothesis".

Neutrinos with only an $L$ component remain massless, as do electrons where the $L$ and $R$ components have different SU(2) assignments; all these states remain massless as the temperature falls below $10^{16}$ degree Celsius or equivalently $10^{12}$ eV. This protection of light chiral states was first suggested in the $(V - A)$ theory of 1958.

For spin-0 particles, chirality cannot be defined because there is no spin for chirality to be defined. The first guess on their mass is therefore very heavy. For a spin-0 particle to travel with light velocity like transversely polarised gauge bosons, its mass must be zero. In Fig. 1, its direction must be in the propagation direction $\pm\hat{z}$ since it should not carry an angular momentum. But, a natural mass of spin-0 particle is non-zero.

Mutton fat aggregation can be postponed by stirring mutton fat melted in water. Spin-$\frac{1}{2}$ fermions with both L- and R-handedness with perfect matching can be stirred with extra conditions, i.e. with more symmetries, such that they survive as massless particles below a temperature of $10^{12}$ eV. Spin-1 gauge bosons are massless because of the gauge symmetry. But, spin-0 scalars are massive.

At this time of temperature 2.7° K, the SM particles are very heavy as shown in Fig. 3 of Chapter 6, with a top quark mass of 173 GeV, which is about million-billion times the current temperature. Even 2.7° is so low compared to the initial temperature at the time of universe creation that the SM particles in the end obtain mass. Looking at Fig. 5 of Chapter 6, there are three questions with one each for particles in the same circular band. First as, the Higgs particle in the centre is related, "How do the SM particles obtain mass?" Second, for the spin-1 particles in the middle, in addition to the gluons discussed in Chapter 7 there is a question, "Why are there just four particles for the mediation of weak and electromagnetic interactions?" Third, for the spin-$\frac{1}{2}$ fermions in the outer band, "Why are there 45 chiral fermions?"

The answer to the second question was the finding of the electroweak gauge symmetry SU(2)×U(1) by Sheldon Glashow (1932–) in 1960. An earlier attempt had been made by Glashow's PhD adviser, Julian Schwinger (1918–1994) in 1957, but he did not have the correct experimental information about weak interactions and so followed a false trail. Sometimes, it is said that it is the unification of weak and electromagnetic forces in the sense that both must be treated in the same gauge symmetry principle. Since Maxwell's electromagnetism of 1865, it was the first and successful unification pulling weak interactions in this arena. But, the SM included two coupling parameters $\alpha_2$ and $\alpha_1$ for the factors SU(2) and U(1), respectively. Unification with just one coupling constant was (unsuccessfully) attempted over a decade later, under the name of grand unified theories (GUTs) of all elementary particle forces, except gravity.

Giving mass to the $W^{\pm}$ and the $Z^0$ proved to be a more difficult problem. In 1960, Glashow wrote that the masses were a "stumbling block" which must be temporarily ignored in his paper, which discovered the electroweak gauge structure of the standard model. This provides an interesting example of solving one crucial problem while deliberately delaying the solution of another.

With the $W^{\pm}$ and the $Z^0$ masses, weak interactions of proton, neutron, muon, and other light fermions are given by Fermi's constant $G_F$ for the weak CC and another coupling for the weak neutral current (NC). Usually, these two couplings are discussed in terms of $G_F$ and the weak mixing angle $\sin^2\theta_W$. So, the first experimental confirmations were centred on fitting all the weak NC experiments in terms of one parameter: the weak mixing angle $\sin^2\theta_W$.

The weak NC was first discovered by the Gargamelle bubble chamber at CERN in 1973. A final hurdle to checking the gauge structure of SU(2)×U(1) was to discover the parity-violating coupling of $Z^0$ to electrons. Note that one aspect of weak interaction is parity violation. This predicted from the $eeZ$ coupling an optical rotation of polarised light traversing certain gases, and in experiments carried out at Seattle and Oxford such a rotation could not be successfully detected. Until 1978, these atomic experiments cast serious doubt on the model.

In 1978, however, a more direct measurement of the $eeZ$ coupling, i.e. the weak NC effect, was completed, involving scattering of polarised electrons off deuterium at SLAC by Charles Prescott (1938–) and Richard Taylor (1929–2018). This brilliant experiment, which detected an effect order of magnitude smaller than the dominant electromagnetic contribution, convinced the particle theory community that the SM is correct after the report by Taylor at the ICHEP 1978 conference in Tokyo, Japan. In fact, in the evening of the closing day of ICHEP 1978, the Japanese National TV broadcasted a documentary on the story of the SM.

With the value 0.233 for $\sin^2\theta_W$ reported a year later at the 1979 International Conference on Neutrinos held at Bergen, Norway, the $Z^0$ mass was predicted to be 91 GeV. The spin-1 gauge boson $Z^0$ with this mass was in fact produced by the Proton–Antiproton Collider at CERN in 1983, which was reported by two experimental groups at CERN, the UA1 group led by Carlo Rubbia (1934–) and the UA2 group. This discovery confirmed the SM experimentally, and the precision NC data on the weak mixing angle 0.233 determined in this period are still correct compared to a more accurate value determined by the recent experiments at the Large Hadron Collider (LHC) of CERN. The gauge boson $W^\pm$ for the source of the weak CC was discovered by the UA1 and UA2 groups of CERN, also in 1983.

Glashow's dilemma, "stumbling block", for the mass of $Z^0$ and $W^\pm$ is the heart of the first problem at the centre of Fig. 5 of Chapter 6. Glashow's "stumbling block" was removed by the so-called Higgs mechanism, which was worked out in 1964 by Francois Englert (1932–), Robert Brout (1928–2011), Peter Higgs (1929–), Gerald Guralnik (1936–2014), Carl Hagen (1937–), and Thomas Kibble (1932–2016).

The Higgs mechanism was correctly used in the SM gauge group SU(2) × U(1). With gauge symmetry, i.e. with massless particles, all gauge bosons have the transverse polarisation as mentioned earlier. Helicity is the rotational sense measured in the direction of propagation: the sense **L** in Fig. 1 is denoted by $-1$ and the sense **R** is denoted by $+1$. A natural mass of spin-0 particle is non-zero. For this spin-0 to combine with the transverse gauge boson, it must have exactly the same property except the spin. First, it is pseudoscalar, having the same gauge transformation property. Second, its direction must be in the propagation direction $\hat{z}$ since it should not carry an angular momentum. Third, it must travel with light velocity to say "Hello" to the transverse gauge boson, moving together in the same direction with light velocity. To travel with light velocity, its mass should be zero. But, we said above that a natural mass of spin-0 particle is non-zero. This condition is evaded if a global symmetry in question is *spontaneously broken.*

To give mass to massless gauge boson, we need polarisation to the longitudinal direction (the forward or backward direction of propagation) in addition to the two transverse degrees of spin-1 gauge boson. Spin-0 pseudoscalars provide these longitudinal degrees. For both gauge bosons $W^{\pm}$ and $Z^0$ to be massive, we must provide three pseudoscalars. But, except the spin difference, all the other properties must be the same. Since these gauge bosons transform non-trivially at least under the SU(2) transformation, we need some pseudoscalars transforming non-trivially under the SU(2) transformation. Steven Weinberg and Abdus Salam suggested that two complex scalars, or four real scalars, are grouped into one complex doublet.

In the interpretation of quantum mechanics by Max Born and Chen Ning Yang in Chapter 5, quantum mechanics is phase mechanics. We are considering spin-1 gauge boson and spin-0 scalar. The gauge transformation on the scalars appear in the phase. So, three scalars appear in the phase, whose number 3 matches the three gauge bosons in SU(2). (As discussed in Chapter 7, there are $N^2 - 1$ gauge bosons for an SU(N) gauge theory.) Out of the four scalars we introduced, where did the remaining one go? It must belong to the real coefficient of the exponential factor. Counting the number of scalars in this way is the unitary gauge since we used the unitary transformation. In this setup, the property of the remaining scalar is the property of vacuum or ground state, which is discovered in technical books as the vacuum expectation value (VEV). If a scalar field gets a VEV and breaks a symmetry, it is called "spontaneous symmetry breaking".

The real scalar is called the Higgs boson and was finally discovered at CERN in 2012 with the mass value 125 GeV. This is the Higgs mechanism, which breaks the SU(2)×U(1) electroweak symmetry to only U(1) electromagnetic symmetry and thereby generates the mass of the $W^{\pm}$ and $Z^0$. Because we used only three pseudoscalars, we cannot make the remaining gauge boson massive as pointed out by Tom Kibble in 1966. This remaining gauge boson is a photon. A major advantage of the Higgs mechanism is that the theory preserves renormalisability proven first by Tiny Veltman (1931–) and Gerard 't Hooft (1946–) and in a more understandable way by Ben Lee (1935–1977) and Jean Zinn-Justin (1943–), which puts the standard model on a footing with QED in that the quantum corrections can be consistently calculated with high accuracy.

From the non-relativistic condensed matter property, the essence of Higgs mechanism was known in the late 1950s to Yoichiro Nambu (1921–2015) and Phillip Anderson (1923–). The road toward the relativistic form of spontaneous symmetry breaking in particle physics, discussed in the above paragraph, was started by Jeffrey Goldstone (1933–) and discussed without local gauge symmetry by Goldstone, Weinberg, and Salam. Peter Higgs used the same form suggested by Goldstone but with the input of local gauge symmetry and found that there remains a physically observable real scalar.

Spontaneous symmetry breaking of gauge symmetries sometimes introduces magnetic monopoles via the so-called Kibble mechanism. At every space point, the VEV of a Higgs field can be assigned. If the VEV is the same everywhere, the effect is making some gauge bosons massive, just by counting which gauge boson obtains the longitudinal degree. In the four-dimensional space–time, we presented the instanton solution as the gauge field values in Chapter 7, as shown in Fig. 4. Now, we consider field values of the Higgs field. Suppose that an unbroken U(1) gauge theory results from spontaneous symmetry breaking. Consideration of $U(1)_{em}$ by breaking the SM gauge group $SU(2)\times U(1)$ does not apply here because we have U(1) before and after the symmetry breaking. Transformation under U(1) is a circle, mathematically denoted as a sphere in one dimension $S_1$.

An interesting situation occurs when one creates an $S_1$ circle out of no circle. In general, the group space of non-abelian simple groups does not have $S_1$. We said that a quantum mechanical transformation is a phase, meaning on the surface of a unit sphere. In this sense, U(1) is sitting on a circle, i.e. the circumference of a two-dimensional sphere disk. The SU(2) instanton solution was sitting on $S_3$, the surface of a four-dimensional sphere. Since we want a localised particle, we consider the surface of three-dimensional sphere, i.e. $S_2$. Any simple group has SU(2) as a subgroup. So, SU(2) group directions can be put on the surface of a three dimensional ball. What will happen if this SU(2) gauge symmetry is broken to U(1) gauge symmetry? For an electric monopole, it is shown in Fig. 1 of Chapter 7. However, Maxwell's equation does not introduce magnetic monopoles, i.e. the magnetic fields do not have ending sources. Can a magnetic monopole appear in case a simple group such as SU(2) breaks to produce a U(1) gauge theory? Yes, it happens because of the Kibble mechanism on the VEVs of Higgs fields in the universe as the universe cools down. It was discovered by 't Hooft (1946–) and Alexander Polyakov (1945–), and the resulting monopole is called a 't Hooft–Polyakov monopole.

The Higgs field has at least four real components such that three parameters can be in the phase, i.e. to associate with an SU(2) symmetry. Then, the VEVs of the Higgs field can have hedgehog-type directions as shown in Fig. 2(a). At the origin, the VEV is zero. Suppose we calculate the outgoing **B** fields as shown there. Indeed, 't Hooft and Polyakov showed that there arises a **B** field proportional to $1/r^2$ at a large radius $r$. There must be a magnetic monopole sitting at the origin. But, U(1) charges are counted by the flux since it is a gauge theory. Suppose we move topologically all **B** fields to a line as shown in Fig. 2(b). Then, the flux is calculated just on the

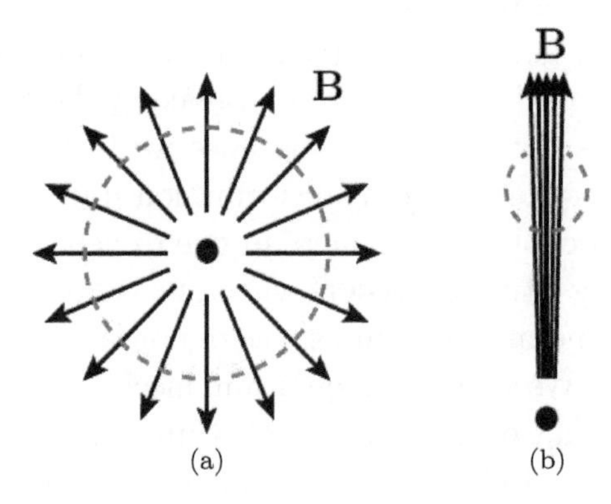


Figure 2: Magnetic monopole.

small disk, and hence by the boundary (red dashed line in Fig. 2(b)) of the disk by the Stokes theorem. So, shifting the phase over a circle must give an identity, $e^{i2\pi \cdot \text{integer}}$ such that one can never see the outgoing flux experimentally. This gives the quantisation condition of the magnetic charge and depends on the VEVs of Higgs fields, i.e. how SU(2) is broken down to U(1). The magnetic monopole mass is of order (VEV)/$e$.

This has a far-reaching consequence in GUTs such as SU(5). SU(5) is broken to the SM containing U(1) factor and hence magnetic monopoles of mass around $10^{16-17}$ GeV should appear if the GUT is the one that nature chose. These heavy monopoles could never have led to our universe as pointed out by John Preskill (1953–). What should we do? Even though the flatness and isotropic problems are counted as the primary reasons now, the monopole problem was used as one motivation for the inflationary scenario by Alan Guth (1947–).

The third question related to the outermost spin-$\frac{1}{2}$ particles of Fig. 5 of Chapter 6 is the flavour problem or the family problem. After obtaining order of hadrons in Chapter 7, it was determined that SU(3) flavour symmetry was established. But, hadrons with flavour SU(3) (or three quarks $u, d$, and $s$) were plagued with the apparently fatal problem of predicting strangeness-changing weak processes too large to agree with experiment. This problem was solved in 1970 by three Harvard physicists, GIM (Sheldon Glashow, John Iliopoulos (1940–), and Luciano Maiani (1941–)), who predicted the existence of a fourth flavour of quark, named charm $c$.[1] The charmed quark was dramatically discovered in the so-called 1974 November Revolution started by Samuel Ting (1936–). Since 1974, Gell-Mann's mathematical quarks were established in the atomic world as a reality.

Two further flavours or quarks, bottom ($b$) and top ($t$), were subsequently discovered in 1977 and 1995, respectively, to accompany three families of charged leptons $e^-, \mu^-, \tau^-$ and neutrinos $\nu_e, \nu_\mu, \nu_\tau$. These are the 45 chiral fermions in the outermost ring in Fig. 5 of

[1] S. L. Glashow, J. Iliopoulos, and L. Maiani, Weak Interactions with Lepton-Hadron Symmetry, *Phys. Rev. D* **2**, 1285 (1970).

Chapter 6. In fact, the same number of families are needed to preserve renormalisability of the SM, as pointed out in 1972.

Three quark families are needed if time reversal symmetry in the SM is required to be broken just by the weak CC interactions. Time reversal is like playing a video of a movie backward. In the SM, time reversal symmetry is like changing a particle to its antiparticle at the opposite point with respect to an origin. It is called CP symmetry. Talking in terms of CP is better for experimentalists since it is difficult for them to make a device with time running in the backward direction. The three-family condition in the SM for the weak CP violation was found by two Japanese physicists Mokoto Kobayashi (1944–) and Toshihide Maskawa (1940–). So far since 2006, experimentalists did not find any hint that we require any additional source for the weak CP violation in particle physics.

Talking in terms of CCs of three families is equivalent to discussing six quarks (three quarks with charge $\frac{2}{3}\,e$ and three quarks with charge $-\frac{1}{3}\,e$) with L-handed chirality only. For equally charged quarks, for example $u, c, t$, quark mixing is possible. The possibility of quark mixing was found by Nicola Cabibbo. General quark mixing relevant for the weak CC interaction needs a $3 \times 3$ unitary matrix. The most general and physically relevant $3 \times 3$ unitary matrix is parametrised by three real angles and a phase, which is called the CKM matrix in which the phase is called the KM phase for which Kobayashi and Maskawa were credited by the Nobel Committee in 2008. Lincoln Wolfenstein (1923–2015) wrote a CKM matrix in 1983 such that it is easily usable by experimentalists, and most hadronic data were analysed using this form. This approximate form is correct for entries in the matrix bigger than 0.01. In 1985, Swedish Cecilia Jarlskog (1941–) noted a simple number $J$ which is the same in any CKM parametrisation. The reason the Nobel Committee credited Kobayashi and Maskawa was because all hadronic experiments converged to giving $J$ at a value little bit smaller than 0.0001. So, there was a need to analyse data with CKM parametrisations which are exactly unitary.

The corresponding leptonic sector also carries three families. There are both chiralities (L and R) of electron, muon, and tau. As already mentioned in an earlier Chapter 5 and Fig. 5 of Chapter 6, the accompanying neutrinos, electron-type neutrino $\nu_e$, muon-type neutrino $\nu_\mu$, and tau-type neutrino $\nu_\tau$ come only with one chirality L. Introduction of neutrinos in 1930 by Wolfgang Pauli (1900–1958) for nuclear $\beta$-decay was for neutrino mass, of the order of nucleon mass, but it was before knowing anything about the stories of the "V–A" quartet. In the SM, therefore, neutrino masses are *zero* at the renormalisable level.

Pauli's bold hypothesis was incorporated into Fermi's theory of weak interactions in 1934 and in all further such theories, although the neutrino was not directly detected until 1956 by Frederick Reines (1918–1998) and Clyde Cowan, (1919–1974) at the Savannah River nuclear reactor in South Carolina. That was what we now call the electron-type antineutrino. In 1962, Leon Lederman (1922–2018), Melvin Schwartz (1932–2006), and Jack Steinberger (1921–) showed experimentally that there were at least two different flavours of neutrino. Now, we have evidence for three, $\nu_e, \nu_\mu, \nu_\tau$, completing the required 45 chiral fields of Fig. 5 of Chapter 6.

In the SM and also in an SU(5) GUT, the neutrinos were assumed to be massless and represented by L-handed Weyl spinors. The massless neutrino would travel at the speed of light and have a definite helicity as mentioned above, i.e. only L-handed according to experiments on $\beta$-decay based on CCs.

Everything changed in 1998 when at the Super-Kamiokande experiment in Japan it was convincingly shown that neutrinos entering the atmosphere changed flavour, or oscillated, possible only with a non-zero mass. Many more experiments have confirmed this and thus there is a non-trivial $3 \times 3$ mixing matrix for the three neutrino types as the CKM matrix in the quark sector, which has spawned a large field of research, especially as it is the only well-established deviation from the original minimal standard model.

In the quark sector, hadron masses come in the discussion of mixing experiments at low energy. In most neutrino experiments, neutrinos travel with almost light velocity and the kinetic energy is more important, and hence mixing experiments use the energy of neutrinos. A correct formula for the neutrino oscillation was given in 1957 by Russian Physicist Bruno Pontecorvo (1913–1993) for an electron-type neutrino to its anti-neutrino because any other neutrino was not known at that time. For neutrinos carrying no electric charge, neutrino and antineutrino oscillation is possible and hence in general a $6 \times 6$ mixing matrix can be considered. But, to discuss it in parallel with the CKM matrix, we neglect the small neutrino–anti-neutrino oscillation, and consider the $3 \times 3$ mixing matrix, following Ziro Maki, Masami Nakagawa, and Shoichi Sakata (1911–1970), which can be called the MNS matrix. Most physicists, however, call it the PMNS matrix, which has three mixing angles and three CP-violating phases. It is irresistible to compare this PMNS matrix with the CKM matrix. The CKM matrix has one CP-violating phase. Two of the three real angles are very small and the largest, the Cabibbo angle, is only about 13°. In the PMNS matrix, by contrast, the mixing angles are much bigger, one being close to maximal (45°), one about 34°, and the smallest being 9°.

This qualitative difference means that in any theory of flavour symmetry, the quarks and leptons must belong to different representations of a discrete flavour group. Another difference is that the neutrino masses are a million times smaller than those for any of the charged leptons and quarks.

Non-zero neutrino masses, in a world with the SM fields only, require non-renormalisable interactions of the SM fields. How these interactions appear depends on the details of a model. Steven Weinberg considered, in effect, a non-renormalisable form for the quark mass matrix in 1977. For a $2 \times 2$ matrix, one diagonal element was very heavy, say $M$, and two off-diagonal elements were small, say $v$, and the remaining diagonal element was zero. Because of the invariance of the determinant, two eigenvalues are approximately given, $M$ and $v^2/M$, which is the basis of the seesaw mechanism that if $M$ goes up, the other goes down. Here, $v$ is considered to be a VEV of some scalar field $\sigma$ and $\frac{1}{M}\bar{d}_L s_R \sigma\sigma + \cdots$ is an effective non-renormalisable interaction. This non-renormalisable quark interaction preserves the baryon number.

The most elegant explanation of the tininess of the neutrino masses is the so-called *seesaw* mechanism, which invokes at least two, usually three, right-handed super-heavy neutrinos as suggested in 1977 by Peter Minkowski. Note here that neutrinos in the SM are only L-handed and the non-renormalisable interactions for masses must be of the Majorana type, breaking lepton number. As far as the seesaw mechanism is concerned, it is the same as above. But, since the non-renormalisable interactions break the lepton number, that breaking must be taken into account. It is done by introducing heavy SU(2)×U(1) singlet neutrinos. So, to confirm, the seesaw mechanism is rendered challenging by the heaviness of the right-handed neutrinos, if they exist. If there were three light neutrinos, one needs three heavy neutrinos in the most straightforward generalisation.

There are two gauge coupling constants in the SM, and hence it is not a true unification of coupling constants. We discussed the parameter, the weak mixing angle put in by hand in the SM. To have one gauge coupling constant, grand unified theories (GUTs) have been considered. In GUTs, therefore, the weak mixing angle $\sin^2\theta_W$ is determined. We recall that the experimentally determined value is close to 0.233 at the electroweak scale.

As Howard Georgi and Sheldon Glashow did in SU(5), we can use all L-handed ones, just replacing R-handed ones (the bullets) of Fig. 5 of Chapter 6 with L-handed antiparticles. This is called a chiral representation since we used only one chirality **L**. This is the magic of quantum field theory (QFT). Georgi and Glashow played the part of magicians. A trick in QFT is that a quantum field defined for a species of a particle can create a particle and can also annihilate its antiparticle. For spin-$\frac{1}{2}$ particles, the opposite chirality is used for antiparticles. Whether we use a quantum field of particle or that of antiparticle, the same is achieved if we wanted to create a particle. If we use the quantum field of the particle, we use the creation operator. On the contrary if we use the quantum field of the antiparticle, then we use the annihilation operator. Another magical effect of QFT is that all electrons created by the electron quantum field are identical, or indistinguishable, in the whole universe.

The 15 chiral fields in one family of Fig. 5 of Chapter 6 are grouped to five and 10 groups such that all electromagnetic charges in each group sum up to zero. That is possible with gauge group SU(5). The collection of five is electron-type neutrino, which is L-handed, L-handed electron, and three colours of anti-*d* quark that are all L-handed. In Fig. 5 of Chapter 6, we used both L-handed particles and R-handed particles, but Georgi and Glashow used a chiral representation for helicity **L**. Then, all bulleted ones are replaced by triangles with opposite charges, both for the electromagnetic and colour charges. Thus, the electromagnetic charge of anti-*d* quark is $+\frac{1}{3}$, and the sum of electromagnetic charges for the members of the group is $(0) + (-1) + \frac{1}{3} + \frac{1}{3} + \frac{1}{3}$, which is zero. For the sum of colour charges, we have to consider two numbers like the third component of isospin and the hypercharge described in Chapter 7, but this time for the colour gauge group $SU(3)_{\rm colour}$. For a triplet or an antitriplet of quarks, sum of colour sisospin is zero, and so it is for colour hypercharge. This group of five is the fundamental representation of group SU(5). The essence of the SU(5) GUT is contained in this collection of five particles.

Charge quantisation is achieved. From the sum of the electromagnetic charges, the electromagnetic charge of *d* quark was determined above as $-\frac{1}{3}$, which determines the electromagnetic charge of *u* quark as $\frac{2}{3}$. So, the charge of proton, i.e. the electromagnetic charge of *uud*, is +1. GUTs solve a long-standing puzzle that the sum of electron and proton charges is zero. If the universe is full of hydrogen atoms, the total charge of the universe is zero. All heavier elements can be manufactured from hydrogen atoms and neutrons which are electrically neutral.

The weak mixing angle $\sin^2\theta_W$ is determined. Basically, the weak mixing angle is given by the ratio of two coupling constants in the SM. Since GUTs have one coupling constant, the ratio is fixed. The SU(5) GUT determines the weak mixing angle as $\frac{3}{8}$. But, this is the case when the unification is still valid. If the GUT group is broken down to the SM gauge group, say at a $10^{16}$-GeV energy scale or at the length scale of $10^{-30}$ cm, the coupling strengths at larger length scales are as shown in Fig. 3. The QCD coupling is shown as the red curve. The SU(2) and U(1) coupling constants are shown as black curves, and the weak mixing angle is a ratio of these two curves. $\frac{3}{8}$ at the

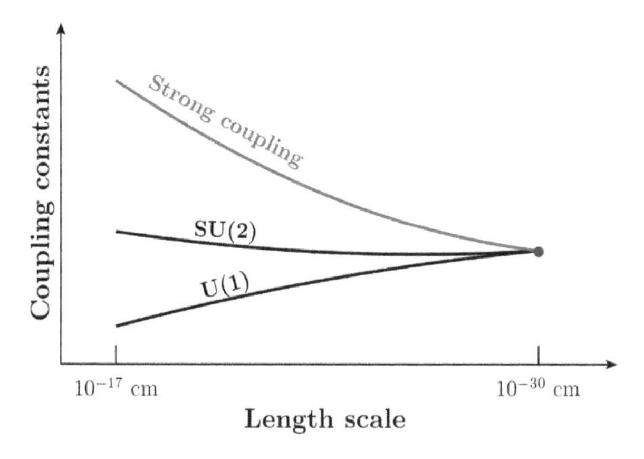


Figure 3: Magnitudes of coupling constants.

GUT scale evolves to a smaller value, ending up close to 0.233 at the electroweak scale. This is one great success of GUTs.

Figure 3 does not explain why we stopped the figure at the length scale of $10^{-17}$ cm. Several high-energy accelerators, including Tevatron of Fermilab and LHC of CERN, confirmed that the value of the strong coupling at $10^{-17}$ cm is about 0.118. If we continue the red curve to larger length scales, we notice that it is O(1) at the length scale of $10^{-14}$ cm. In fact, strong interactions at low energy are determined by physics at the $10^{-14}$ cm, and we do not discuss physics in terms of quarks for length scales larger than the proton size. This can be applied to electroweak physics if some gauge coupling constant becomes O(1) at the scale $10^{-18}$ cm. The corresponding curve is not shown in Fig. 3. This kind of idea was called "technicolour" in the late 1970s by Leonard Susskind (1940–) and Steven Weinberg, which is a suggestion for generating the hierarchy of two scales, $10^{-30}$ and $10^{-17}$ cm. This method uses dimensionless coupling constant to generate the length scale (or mass scale) when couplings become O(1) under the name of dimensional transmutation. This method, however, does not give the observed quark and lepton masses, and failed in the flavour problem.

To give quark and lepton masses correctly, the Yukawa couplings by Higgs field is definitely needed. In fact, the Higgs boson was discovered at the LHC of CERN in 2012.

Before listing open questions, we comment on the attempts to understand the hierarchy problem. Since the hierarchy is so huge, of order $10^{16}$ in terms of ratio of scales, exponential factor was preferred. In Chapter 6, supersymmetry and superstring were discussed in this regard.

One attempt was introducing some kind of curvature in higher dimensions. If the curvature is extremely large for some internal dimensions and zero for our four-dimensional universe, there may arise an exponential factor. This idea was proposed with warped space by Lisa Randall (1962–) and Raman Sundrum (1964–). The exponential factor is introduced in the ansatz on the metric as $e^{-k|y|}$, where $y$ is roughly the size of the internal space. Newton's constant for gravity $G_{\rm Newton}$ is discussed in terms of the Planck mass, $M_P = 1/\sqrt{8\pi G_{\rm Newton}} = 2.43 \times 10^{18}$ GeV in the natural unit. Its inverse may be taken as the Planck length $\frac{1}{2} \cdot 10^{-32}$ cm. The scale for the internal space may be taken as a string length $10^{-32}$ cm, or something else. An exponential factor of $10^{-16}$ is obtained from $e^{-k|y|}$ for $k|y| \simeq 36.84$. Who fixes this value of 36.84? Is this another tuning or not? Suppose that we change it to 35. Then, the exponential factor is $6.3 \times 10^{-16}$, corresponding to $Z^0$ boson mass of 573 GeV. Suppose that we change it to 40. Then, the exponential factor is $0.0042 \times 10^{-16}$, corresponding to $Z^0$ boson mass of 0.38 GeV. It seems that there is no *a priori* condition fixing this value of the internal space of $k|y| \simeq 36.84$. It belongs to God's design on the size of internal space.

Another attempt at introducing an exponential factor was a confining force of Weinberg and Susskind under the name of technicolour. But, it failed miserably in flavour physics. For flavour physics, scalars are assigned chirality by the $N = 1$ supersymmetry. The supersymmetry idea needs a confining force again to break supersymmetry. Here, the problem was how to generate the scale 246 GeV for the VEV of Higgs doublet. The best idea is again the dimensional transmutation mentioned along with Fig. 3. If there is a new confining force in the hidden sector, it is required to confine above $10^{10}$ GeV as shown in Fig. 4. This picture is drawn without taking into account the gravitational interaction mentioned in Chapter 6. If a scalar develops a VEV at $5 \times 10^{10}$ GeV, the effect of gravity will induce the

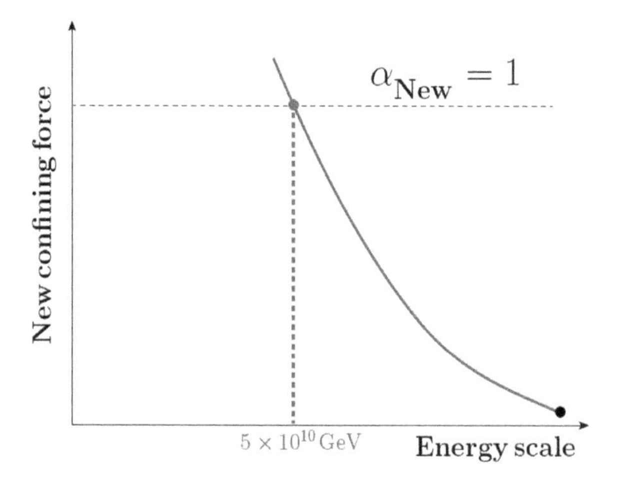


Figure 4: A new confining force from the hidden sector.

superpartner masses of order $(5 \times 10^{10})^2/2.43 \times 10^{18}$ GeV, which is about 1,000 GeV. If a scalar develops a VEV at $10^{11}$ GeV, the effect of gravity will induce the superpartner masses of order 4,000 GeV. Realising this kind of hierarchy solution with supersymmetry is not ruled out yet and even higher energy data are needed. The coupling at the black bullet determines all physics scales below it. Who determined that value of $\alpha_{\mathbf{New}}$? It is determined in relation to the other couplings of the SM in some ultraviolet completed theories. In this sense, this idea belongs to Darwinism.

In the last two paragraphs, we showed two examples of possible gauge hierarchy solutions. It seems that the theory may lie midway between Darwin and Shakespeare.

# Chapter 9

# Open Questions

At the end of the 19th century, a famous physicist proclaimed that fundamental physics was a closed book, essentially finished, on the basis of Newton's classical mechanics and Maxwell's formulation of classical electrodynamics. In 1900, Lord Kelvin said, "There is nothing new to be discovered in physics now. All that remains is more and more precise measurement." This optimism was quickly shown to be premature because in the first quarter of the 20th century the discoveries of quantum mechanics and relativity showed that the theories of Newton and Maxwell were seriously incomplete, although still applicable within restricted domains of the relevant parameters.

No sensible physicist would make a similar proclamation as we approach the end of the first quarter of the 21st century because the standard model of particle theory is evidently not a candidate to be, in any sense, a final theory. Mainly, the problem is that there are so many free parameters which have to be fitted to experiment. Once this is done, the theory is spectacularly successful. But, a final theory should explain the values of most or all the parameters, so we shall discuss them and ideas that have been used to attempt to make further progress without complete success. The many open questions exhibited in the present chapter will make it clear that particle theory, far from being a closed book, is full of very interesting projects for future research.

Let us enumerate the free parameters in the standard model of particle theory. There are six flavours each of quarks and leptons, none of their masses explained by our present understanding, so those are 12 masses which have resisted every attempt at their calculation from theory. This has been called *the scandal of the fermion masses.* It is amazing and humbling that we still do not understand the peculiar fermion spectrum. There are mini-hierarchies for both quarks and leptons, but that is merely a qualitative statement. If some physicist could provide a convincing derivation of, for example, the mass ratio $M_\mu/M_e$, it would be transformative.

The mixing matrices for the quarks and leptons have, respectively, four and six parameters; some limited success has been achieved in calculating these from flavour symmetries. There are the three gauge coupling constants for the groups $SU(3) \times SU(2) \times U(1)$. Two more parameters are needed to describe the electroweak symmetry breaking; we can use, for example, the mass of the $W$ (near 80 GeV) and the mass of the Higgs boson (close to 125 GeV). Finally, there is the strong CP parameter $\bar{\Theta}$ which must be very small for consistency with experiment, for example, the neutron electric dipole moment.

This list completes the total of 28 free parameters to be fitted by experiment. Surely a more complete theory will allow most of these to be calculated from deeper principles? We shall discuss the parameters in more detail below.

There are other unanswered questions. The standard model describes successfully only 5% of the energy in the universe. 95% of the mass energy of the universe is in the form of the mysterious dark matter and dark energy. The matter–antimatter asymmetry of the universe has not been satisfactorily explained. Gravity has not been incorporated. The existence of three fermion families is not explained in the standard model.

Let us begin with the cosmological open questions. The dark side which makes up 95% of the energy is by far the biggest question, including both about 70% dark energy and about 25% dark matter. Dark energy is the more mysterious of the two so we begin with it.

The need for the large majority component of dark energy was discovered in 1998 when it became established that the expansion of the visible universe is accelerating. This was unexpected because almost everybody expected a deceleration, as suggested by a very naïve application of energy conservation. To illustrate this expectation, a *deceleration* parameter had been defined, which now must be assigned a negative value! In the Friedmann expansion equation, which is an Einstein field equation for the special case of homogeneity and spherical symmetry, the observed accelerated expansion is most simply interpreted as a non-zero cosmological constant. There are alternative ideas, but the cosmological constant is certainly the simplest and remains consistent with all observations.

The cosmological constant has a century-old history going back to Einstein who published his general relativity theory in 1916. The following year, he predicted the existence of gravitational waves, which were discovered exactly 100 years later in 2016. The following year, 1917, Einstein applied his new gravitational theory to cosmology and found that his minimal field equations led to an expanding universe. At the time, based on his knowledge of the observational data, Einstein believed that the universe was static and therefore added an extra term to allow a time-independent solution. This choice was unfortunate for two reasons. First, his static solution was unsatisfactory, being unstable under infinitesimal perturbations. Second, there already existed some observational evidence acquired by Melvin Slipher (1875–1969), since 1912, unknown to Einstein in 1917, that hinted at cosmological expansion. It also hinted that the observed nebulae which were blurry and dim patches of light were really other galaxies outside of ours.

One question unsettled at the time was whether the visible universe is only our galaxy of the Milky Way or if is it bigger. The correct answer is that the universe is *much* bigger, as much as the Milky Way itself is larger than the Solar System. The eventually observed signal of expansion was the observation that there is a strong preponderance of redshifted spectra, meaning a recessional velocity, over blueshifted spectra, which signal approach. The redshift is partially due to the familiar Doppler effect, but a more important contribution arises from the stretching of space itself.

Such an expansion was evidenced by the Slipher data, which also provoked the idea that some of the galaxies were outside our galaxy. The true situation became clarified in the subsequent decade of the 1920s, culminating in the results by Edwin Hubble, who confirmed that there were many further galaxies outside the Milky Way and that on average their recession velocity is approximately proportional to their distance. This is Hubble's Law and the slope of the velocity/distance line is called Hubble's constant which has been measured with increasing accuracy since then.

The present value of the Hubble constant is about 70 in the appropriate units. Hubble's value was nearer to 500 because he did not know the distances well. During the second half of the 20th century, values as disparate as 50 and 100 were obtained by different groups. Even today, different methods show a statistically highly significant disagreement between values of about 68 and 72. Sorting out this discrepancy could reveal important information.

When Einstein visited California in January 1931, he met Hubble and studied his data, coming to the conclusion that adding the cosmological constant in his 1917 paper had been a big blunder. Between 1931 and 1998, the term was occasionally reconsidered based on temporary puzzles about the age of the universe. Since 1998, however, we know that there definitely is a non-zero positive and tiny cosmological term, or something very similar, and that is now called dark energy.

It is too generous to credit Einstein with dark energy because it is based on observational data discovered much later than 1955, when he died, but he did understand that such a possibility was consistent with the symmetries of his general relativistic field equations. The 1998 discovery of accelerated expansion was originally made based on measurements of distant supernovae and comparing their redshift distance with a Hubble plot. The most distant supernovae were distinctly fainter than predicted by the Hubble Law. Since then, several other measurements involving the (cosmic microwave background CMB) and acoustic baryon oscillations confirm the result, which can now be derived without reference to supernovae.

From the theoretical point of view, the biggest surprise is that the value of the cosmological constant is 120 orders of magnitude smaller than suggested by estimates based on naïve but plausible versions of quantum gravity, for which we do not have a complete theory. This exceedingly small value is more surprising than the previously believed value of zero, which might be the result of an undiscovered symmetry.

The extremely small value has not been explained and remains one of the biggest challenges in all of theoretical physics. Just to mention one attempt, in superstring theory, there exist a huge number of candidate vacua with energy densities ranging from suitably tiny up to the enormous Planck scale. One interpretation is that there exist a huge number of universes, in what is dubbed a *multiverse*, and for the benefit of life, we live in a universe with the observed value of cosmological constant. This goes under the name *anthropic principle* and we leave our reader to make an assessment of its value. Many of us regard the anthropic principle as outside of science and not much more than an empty explanation.

The anthropic principle, if taken very seriously, implies that it is useless to try to calculate the cosmological constant, which is merely an *environmental* property of our universe. The same conclusion could be reached for the masses of the quarks and leptons, which would then be random numbers whose values are likewise beyond hope of computation. This is a very defeatist and negative viewpoint. The anthropic principle is not helpful in increasing human understanding and we shall not discuss it further. From the scientific point of view, both the multiverse and the anthropic principle might be seen as acts of intellectual desperation.

Dark energy has a negative pressure which signals a repulsive gravity. The ratio of the negative pressure to its energy density is called the *equation of state of dark energy*, denoted by $\omega$. A cosmological constant corresponds to $\omega = -1$. Another approach to dark energy is to invoke a scalar field theory, called quintessence, which gives rise to $\omega > -1$ and predicts a time or redshift dependence of the dark energy. At present, there is no evidence to support this.

Yet another possibility is phantom dark energy with $\omega < -1$. This has the property that, if $\omega$ remains constant, the universe will end after a finite time at a Big Rip. This has problems with negative energy densities, which are challenging to interpret. It requires that time "ends" at a finite time in the future as the universe grows faster exponentially to an infinite size. This scenario has interesting implications for cyclic cosmology where the expansion and contraction of the universe repeat an infinite number of times.

Cyclic cosmology is an alternative to the Big Bang and can avoid the associated initial singularity. At the beginnings of theoretical cosmology, most of the leading theorists, including Einstein himself, favoured cyclicity until Richard Tolman (1881–1948) discovered an apparently insuperable hurdle presented by Boltzmann's second law of thermodynamics. Since this second law requires that the entropy of the universe increases monotonically, the implication would be that the cycles become larger and longer in the future, and smaller and shorter in the past. If one then goes sufficiently far in the past, there must be a Big Bang whose avoidance was the whole idea! This no-go theorem was proved by Tolman in 1931 and largely dissuaded research into cyclicity until the discovery of dark energy in 1998.

Just to illustrate the 20th century disappearance of cyclic cosmology, there was, around 1960, a competition between the Big Bang and Continuous Creation which avoided expansion. This was decided in favour of the Big Bang by the discovery in 1964 of the CMB. It was regarded as a simple dichotomy when it was really a trichotomy with the third possibility being cyclic cosmology, never mentioned at that time.

With the discovery of dark energy, new possibilities appeared to circumvent the Tolman theorem and now the dichotomy is between a "bang" or a "bounce", with the latter perhaps acquiring momentum. The cyclic cosmology has four stages: expansion, turnaround, contraction, and bounce. The entropy argument that originally used to disfavour such an infinite cyclicity can now be countered by the jettisoning of entropy at the turnaround.

Although the bounce is an attractive alternative to the bang, it is challenging to discriminate between the two by observation. The only sharp prediction of the bounce is that $\omega = -1$ very precisely, while a small range of $\omega$ close to $\omega = -1$ is allowed by the bang. Thus, finding $\omega \neq -1$ observationally would disfavour the bounce. Present observational data are fully consistent with $\omega = -1$ and there is no evidence for any redshift variation in the dark energy.

Dark energy is a big challenge to theory and may hold a clue to the correct approach to quantum gravity. There is no satisfactory theory of quantum gravity, which is absent from the standard model of particle theory. Effects of quantum gravity are expected to be infinitesimally small, and without experimental clues, it is problematic to know how to proceed in formulating a mathematical theory.

Nevertheless, dark energy has dramatically changed our view of theoretical cosmology whose practitioners can only be humbled by the realisation that the majority of the universe's energy content is a total mystery. It has put life back into the hitherto abandoned idea of cyclic cosmology with infinite numbers of turnarounds and bounces, and which can avoid the unpleasantness of an initial singularity in the Big Bang theory. The ultimate fate, as well as the origin, of the universe is at issue.

One ambitious approach to quantum gravity is a top-down approach relying only on mathematical elegance. Historically, this has never worked and all successful theories were built on experimental phenomenology. But, there can always be a first time and many workers have spent half a century trying, so far unsuccessfully, to exploit superstring theory.

The history of superstrings from 1968 to 2019 is unusual. It started in 1968 with an inspired mathematical guess, the Veneziano model, for the strong interaction S-matrix. This guess of a simple closed form which satisfied many constraints was a big surprise including to the first author who had just finished a doctoral thesis on strong interactions. He then moved on to a postdoctoral position at Chicago where Yoichiro Nambu quickly understood the string interpretation of the Veneziano model.

This model was used initially in strong interaction phenomenology and called the dual resonance model. It was popular from 1968 to 1974 when, as a theory of strong interactions, it was replaced by QCD. It was shown, especially by Nambu in 1968, that the physical basis for the "magic" formula lies in strings which are one-dimensional extended objects generalising the notion of point particles.

The string theory became superstring theory by the introduction of supersymmetry in the 1970s. Supersymmetry was also applied to the standard model to create the (minimal supersymmetric standard model MSSM) which led to a rich phenomenology. It was further applied to general relativity to create supergravity in 1976.

It was highly non-trivial that such a generalisation of general relativity was possible, and supergravity shows that supersymmetry might have a natural place in nature. Supergravity plays a crucial role in superstring theory and is one limit in 11 space–time dimensions of M-theory to be discussed shortly.

The elegance is, however, by itself insufficient to guarantee that it can connect to the real world. Paul Dirac used to say the beauty of the equations is extremely important in identifying the correct theory. But, one of Dirac's own theories seems to provide a counterexample. In 1931, he proposed a beautiful extension of Maxwell's equations which was more symmetric between electricity and magnetism. This required the existence of magnetic monopoles, which were only either a north pole or a south pole, not a combination of both as has always been observed. Many searches have been made to discover the elusive magnetic monopole.

In 1982, such a search at Stanford, using a (superconducting quantum interference device SQUID) on February 14th found one event which seemed clearly to show the passage of a monopole through the SQUID. In April 1982, the experimentalist presented the event at an international conference in Chapel Hill and convinced a distinguished audience including two Nobel Prize winners that it was real.

The first-named author was asked by the professional journal *Physics Today* to seek a suitable quote from Dirac himself, who at age 80 was at Florida State University in Tallahassee. Dirac was unaware of the "discovery", but was clearly skeptical after waiting over half a century for a confirmation of his theory. His quote was, "I'll believe it only when they bring me one in a bottle."

As time progressed and more sensitive experiments were unable to reproduce the result, it transpired that Dirac was correct. This is a perfect example of an elegant and beautiful theory which is apparently not adopted by nature. It remains to be seen whether supersymmetry is a similar case, but what is by now clear is that supersymmetry broken at the TeV scale or below, as required to address the lightness of the Higgs boson, probably does not exist.

This triad of theories, supersymmetry, supergravity, and superstrings, which can be called super-theories, has been a dominant theme in theoretical physics for over 40 years and their mathematical consistency is very impressive. The leader in superstring effort has been Edward Witten who has acted as a Pied Piper, inspiring many younger physicists to work on string theory. The super-theories play a strong role in deciding funding and faculty hiring, so it has become a self-perpetuating enterprise which has resulted in wonderful mathematics, including great progress in pure mathematics, but whose connection to the real world remains frustratingly lacking even after half a century.

In the history of theoretical physics, there is no precedent for such a complicated and alluringly consistent mathematical structure, that has so many tantalising glimpses of real physics, to have existed, without fulfilling its promise. Superstrings contain, in some sense, the mathematics of general relativity and Yang–Mills theory which underly the standard model and Witten himself has argued that such a theory must therefore apply to the real world. Only time will tell. Witten was awarded in 1990 the Fields Medal, which is the most prestigious prize in mathematics, the first physicist to receive it.

Superstrings received a shot in the arm in 1984 when it was realised that only five specific superstrings were consistent. The first author's 1974 book on dual resonance models initially sold only 1,200 copies since nobody was interested. When the same book was reissued in 1986, it quickly sold 4,000 despite being 12 years out of date. Evidently, the thousands of new young superstring theorists thought that it might contain gold nuggets despite its obsolescence.

Superstrings are fully consistent only in 10 space–time dimensions because only then is the generalised Lorentz invariance non-anomalous. Since we live in only four large space–time dimensions, it is necessary that six spatial dimensions be compactified to a sufficiently small size that they would have escaped detection. This generalises an idea of Kaluza and Klein in the early days of general relativity when they added one additional space dimension to attempt, partially successfully, to unify Maxwell's electromagnetism with gravity.

In 1985, suitable six-dimensional Calabi–Yau manifolds were discovered, which allowed a consistent compactification of the superstring theory and at first it showed some similarity with the standard model. At the time, enthusiasm that it could possibly explain some or all of the free parameters in the particle theory was temporarily at an all-time high.

In 1995, it became established that superstring theory necessarily contains higher-dimensional entities called membranes and Witten showed that all five known superstrings were equivalent, all being limits of an underlying theory called by Witten, M-theory, where M might denote Membrane. An explicit form of such an M-theory has yet to be established and only certain limits thereof are understood. Part of the problem is that in the limits, at least some couplings are small and so can be treated perturbatively, while in a more general domain of M-theory, no couplings are small.

As time progressed, the apparent uniqueness of superstrings or M-theory became much more fuzzy when it was realised that there are a gigantic number, $10^{500}$ or more, of candidate vacua, so the chance of making sharp predictions became more remote. More recently, it has been discussed that in addition to the so-called landscape scenario of superstring vacua, there is also a so-called swampland of vacua which may appear in effective field theories but not have the availability of a consistent ultra-violet completion because of not being in the superstring landscape.

As one example, the minimal standard model of particle theory lies in the swampland unless quintessence-type scalars fields are added. This need not be a fatal problem for M-theory because their compatification usually gives a lot of scalars which can act like quintessence, and could tell us what additional scalars to look for in experiment. Although we may only sit and admire the astonishing mathematical consistency of superstings and M-theory, and support their pursuit, we can say that, if anything, the distance from real-world phenomenology seems as great in 2020 as it was in 1985. Only time will tell whether string theory and its top-down idea can succeed.

This discussion of super-theories provides a natural segue to the next topic of dark matter. Dark matter must be stable or at least have a lifetime longer than the age of the universe. It does not experience strong or electromagnetic interaction, hence has no electric charge or colour. In some theories of dark matter, it experiences weak interactions.

Dark matter certainly experiences gravity, which is how it was discovered in the Coma galaxy cluster by Fritz Zwicky (1898–1974) using the virial theorem in 1933 and more generally in galaxies, by the study of rotational curves, by Vera Rubin (1928–2016) and collaborators in the 1970s.

Zwicky was a creative astrophysicist at Caltech who provided many original ideas. The virial theorem related the kinetic and potential energies of a gravitationally bound system. The Coma cluster contains over 1,000 galaxies and is about 100 Mpc from the Earth. Zwicky found that the galaxies in the cluster were moving too quickly to be bound by the visible matter unless about 90% of the total mass is invisible. He called it *dark matter*, although it was not until the 1970s that its existence was generally accepted.

In galaxies, if the luminous stars were all the matter, the velocities of outlying stars would fall off with distance. What Rubin's group showed, however, after the study of a number of different galaxies, is that this consequence of Newton's law does not happen and considerably more, five times more, gravitating invisible matter must be invoked for consistency. This dark matter which, unlike stars, does not radiate is the issue.

A leading candidate for the dark matter constituent is the (weakly interacting massive particle WIMP). This hypothetical particle is expected to have a mass between 100 and 1,000 GeV and to experience weak interactions. Why should dark matter experience weak interactions? This is inspired by the supersymmetric MSSM, which contains a partner neutralino with spin-$\frac{1}{2}$ and weak interactions. It is stabilised by a discrete $Z_2$ symmetry motivated by proton stability. This provided, already in the 1980s, an ideal candidate for dark matter. Many experiments have been constructed to search for WIMPs, so far without a reproducible result.

There are second and third principal candidates for dark matter. The second is related to one of the 28 free parameters in the standard model, the strong CP phase. One ingenious idea to avoid unobserved CP violation in strong interactions is to postulate a global U(1) symmetry that allows the vacuum to relax to a CP-conserving one. Spontaneous breaking of this symmetry leads to a light pseudoscalar called an axion. The second author wrote a pivotal paper on this subject in 1979.

The axion provides an attractive candidate to be the constituent of dark matter because it is motivated by a shortcoming of the minimal standard model of particle theory. Many experiments are underway to attempt to verify that axions exist is a very light mass range. Superstring theory can contain hundreds or even thousands of candidates for similar light scalars in the form of dilatons or moduli and these are generically called (axion-like particles ALPs), although this is strictly a misnomer because they are scalars rather than pseudoscalars and cannot be axions of the type used to solve the Strong CP Problem.

Nevertheless, the linkage to solution of the strong CP problem provides a good motivation for axions. Some physicists avoid this linkage and consider dark matter to be composed of ultra-light ALPs, many orders of magnitudes smaller in mass based on certain anomalies in cosmological structure formation such as cusps at galactic centres and too many satellite galaxies. This is an example of particle theory inspired by astronomy.

The third and last dark matter candidate we discuss here is the (primordial black hole PBH). This requires a little more discussion.

Black holes in the universe fall into two types: the first is the result of gravitational collapse of a massive star. The second type of black hole (PBH) is formed in the early universe as a result of high density and very large inhomogeneities and fluctuations.

The dark matter cannot all be formed by the former type of black hole because of the baryon number of the universe, which is well known from (big bang nucleosynthesis BBN) calculations. Baryons comprise less than 5% of the total, while the dark matter is 25%. Thus, only PBHs, not gravity-collapse black holes, are a serious candidate to be *all* the dark matter.

There are several observational constraints which suggest their mass is in the intermediate range $20\,M_\odot$ to $2000\,M_\odot$. The best way to discover intermediate mass range PIMBHs is by microlensing, which was shown to be viable for PBHs up to $20M_\odot$ in a famous experiment done in the 1990s by the MACHO Collaboration at Mount Stromlo Observatory near Canberra in Australia.

An experiment underway at the Blanco 4-m telescope at Cerro Tololo in Northern Chile uses the DECam, a camera installed to study dark energy in the (dark energy survey DES). This camera was originally financed by Fermilab in the USA after its Tevatron shut down and it chose dark energy as its new mission. The results of the DES, completed in 2018, were frustrating in that the dark energy equation of state is consistent with $\omega = -1$ and with no measurable redshift dependence with the accuracy available. The telescope is more powerful than that used in Australia to search for MACHO dark matter, and the DECam is a huge 520-megapixel camera, so there is every reason to believe this experiment can confirm $DM = PIMBHs$, if it is correct. If so, it would be revolutionary to astronomy and cosmology and would frustrate all terrestrial experiments to directly detect dark matter in the form of WIMPs or axions.

The deep reason why so many PIMBHs may be formed in the early universe is entropy. Entropy is not usually mentioned in papers on particle theory because a single particle cannot meaningfully be assigned entropy, which is a statistical concept usually involving a very large number of particles. One exception is a black hole which possesses an exceptionally large entropy, the largest possible for an object of its size.

If we study the entropy of the objects known in the universe, an overwhelming majority comes from the supermassive black holes at the galactic centres. The fraction is very nearly one, differing from one by only a fraction 0.000000000000001. Increasing this entropy by a significant factor, say 1,000, is possible only if the dark matter is made from PIMBHs.

Thus, we may assume that nature chooses dynamics which can substantially increase entropy in the early universe and the most efficient concentration of entropy occurs in black holes.

Both dark energy and dark matter are challenges to any aspiring particle theorist as there is by now no clear separation between cosmology and particle theory, especially as they merge together in the high temperatures of the early universe.

To return from the cosmos to the microscopic world of old-fashioned particle theory, we now systematically re-examine the status of the remaining parameters in the standard model. Two of them, $M_W$ and $M_H$, describe the electroweak symmetry breaking. Here, there is another important open question: why is $M_H = 125\,\text{GeV}$ so light? There is every reason to believe theoretically that $M_H$ should be much higher, at the GUT scale $\sim 10^{16}\,\text{GeV}$ or the Planck scale $\sim 10^{19}\,\text{GeV}$.

This is the famous hierarchy problem. In its heyday, supersymmetry offered to solve this, but its power was exaggerated because although supersymmetry renders the hierarchy technically natural, it does not really explain it and it must still be put in by hand. So, the lightness of the Higgs mass is certainly one open question.

The point is that the Higgs boson is the only spin-zero particle in the menu of the standard model. In perturbation theory, its mass develops a quadratic divergence unlike higher spin (1/2 or 1) particles with only a logarithmic divergence which can be absorbed in the renormalisation process.

For the spin-zero Higgs boson, the mass is expected to be at the high-energy cutoff due to new physics, and this can be arbitrarily high. It is a deep mystery why the mass is as low as 125 GeV. An optimistic interpretation is that there *must* exist new physics at a relatively low scale, say a few TeV, to act as a cutoff in the quantum corrections to the scalar mass.

On the contrary, we know that radiative corrections to electroweak interactions demand a scalar close to the observed mass so any far higher mass would not work. Nevertheless, it is a conceptual problem to question why the mass has not been swept off to some unobservable higher scale. Although the particle appears as if elementary and a sole spin-zero state, perhaps there are other similar states in a similar mass region. No evidence exists for this.

A different approach to this is to assume the Higgs boson is composite and arises as a bound state due to an unknown strong force, stronger than QCD, called technicolour. Attempts to build such a consistent model have usually failed, although for a long time it was considered the alternative to supersymmetry. By now, neither approach has been entirely successful which means that the light Higgs mass remains a deep, open question.

Our next three parameters are the gauge couplings $\alpha_i(\mu)$ with $i = 1, 2, 3$ of the standard model. These can be related by grand unification in a GUT group like SU(5) or SO(10), which has only one progenitor coupling. Alternatively, we can use a quiver theory where the GUT scale may be as low as 4 TeV with an ameliorated hierarchy.

It is an attractive idea that the gauge group $SU(3)_C \times SU(2)_L \times U(1)_Y$ should be subsumed into a simple group. The way in which triangle anomalies in the standard model are cancelled between quarks and leptons also suggests that they belong in common representations of the unifying gauge group. This is true for the $\mathbf{10} + \bar{\mathbf{5}}$ of SU(5) and for the **16** of SO(10). The minimal SU(5) GUT looked golden from its invention in 1974 until the lower limit on the proton lifetime disagreed with theory in 1984.

This failure of the simplest GUT came as a surprise to the particle theory community, the majority of whom expected proton decay to occur as predicted by SU(5). In hindsight, it was a huge assumption that there would be no new physics in the 12 orders of magnitude in energy between the weak scale and the GUT scale. Nevertheless, many of us suspect that there is some truth in grand unification, which lacks only the correct way of implementation.

Gauge groups suggestive of GUT arise naturally as subgroups of the exceptional group $E_8$, which occurs in the compactification of the heterotic superstring. This fact gave rise to all the excitement of the mid-1980s when everything appeared to be coming together and the parameters in the SM appeared to conceivably be calculable. In hindsight, the uniqueness of string theory was overestimated.

Regarding the quark-mixing matrix which has three mixing angles $\theta_i$ and one CP-violating phase $\delta_{\rm KM}$, one procedure which has been at least partially successful is the use of a discrete flavour symmetry. In this way, a fit to the angles can be achieved. Similarly in the leptonic PMNS matrix, the angles can be understood.

Ideally, the same flavour symmetry applies to both the quarks and the leptons. Many papers treat only the leptons because they are simpler but that can access only the lepton-mixing matrix. Clearly, it is better simultaneously to fit both the quark- and lepton-mixing matrices. This is possible using, for example, the binary tetrahedral group $T'$.

The quark- and lepton-mixing matrices have quite different hierarchies and to accommodate both requires different assignments for the leptons, for which triplets are adequate, and the quarks, for which doublets are necessary to distinguish the third family which couples only very weakly to the first two families.

The quark-mixing matrix is not very different from a unit matrix, the main difference being the (small) Cabibbo angle between the first and second quark families. The lepton-mixing matrix is nothing like a unit matrix with even a near maximal mixing between the second and third families and a large mixing between the first and second.

Nevertheless, by using flavour symmetries, the three mixing angles $\theta_i$ $(i = 1, 2, 3)$ of the quark-mixing matrix and the $\Theta_j$ $(j = 1, 2, 3)$ of the lepton-mixing matrix can be successfully fitted or predicted. The CP-violating phase $\delta_{\rm KM}$ in CKM can be understood, while the three CP phases in the PMNS matrix are less well measured.

The biggest failure of flavour symmetry is with regard to the lepton and quark masses. Somehow, the mixings are more accessible than the masses. Probably, it is fair to say that the lack of progress in predicting, or postdiction, of these masses remains the most challenging problem in going beyond the standard model.

We may state that it is the 12 fermion masses for which every attempt has been frustrated. In an anthropic approach, they could be random numbers. Of course, there is a hierarchical pattern in the family structure, but this is insufficient to make quantitative estimates for the masses.

The families of quarks $(u, d)$, $(c, s)$, and $(t, b)$ clearly become successively heavier with $(u, d)$ being very light and most important to everyday life and to the universe. The top quark $t$ is surprisingly heavy, close to the electroweak symmetry breaking scale. This has led some physicists to speculate that the Higgs boson might be a bound state of top–antitop, but detailed calculations have so far disfavoured this attractive idea. The top is so heavy that it decays too fast to become a bound toponium state analogous to charmonium and bottomonium, which provide nearly non-relativistic systems for studying QCD.

The top quark stands out only partly because of its surprisingly large mass, the most massive of all the elementary particles. Its mass is the most accurately known of all the quarks, to within a percent. Its mass, together with the Higgs mass, plays the dominant role in the effective potential of the standard model. This in turn determines whether the vacuum is absolutely stable.

Shortly after the Higgs boson was discovered in 2012 and its mass determined to be close to 125 GeV, detailed calculations in 2013 revealed that the electroweak vacuum, in the absence of any new physics, is metastable! This result is sensitive to the masses $M_H$ and $M_t$. If the Higgs mass was just 2 GeV higher, 127 GeV instead of 125 GeV, or if the top quark was 2 GeV lower, 171 GeV instead of 173 GeV, the vacuum would be absolutely stable.

Even if the vacuum is metastable, its lifetime is very much longer than the age of the universe, as much as $\sim 10^{100}$ years! But, there is a question here of whether the metastability is a clue to the origin of electroweak symmetry breaking and perhaps, after all, there is a special significance to the heavy top quark mass.

There are a couple of other open questions. One is the matter–antimatter asymmetry of the universe where there is a huge preponderance of matter over antimatter when we expect that matter and antimatter were in equal amounts in the very early universe. Three criteria were listed by Sakharov (1921–1989) in 1967 which could allow formation of a suitable asymmetry: (i) B violation; (ii) C and CP violation; and (iii) thermal disequilibrium. The last (iii) follows from the expansion in the early universe. Grand unified theories usually have (i). The CP violation in the standard model is too small to generate adequate asymmetry, so an additional source of CP violations is needed.

Recent work on the quantum mechanical treatment of black holes gives one hint of a new source of CP violation and it remains to be checked whether this can help with the matter–antimatter asymmetry. As an alternative to grand unification with B violation, a possibility is to create lepton number L in the CP-violating decay of heavy right-handed neutrinos as appear in the seesaw mechanism. This is called leptogenesis and the L asymmetry is subsequently converted to the required B asymmetry in the electroweak phase transition by non-perturbative effects.

It is a striking fact of cosmology that all known galaxies are composed of matter, not antimatter. If this were not the case, there would be evidence from copious gamma rays produced by matter–antimatter annihilation. Assuming, as is plausible, that in the very early universe antimatter was created symmetrically with matter, the subsequent annihilation was not complete and a relatively tiny amount, less than one part per billion, of the matter survived and is of what the observed galaxies and us are made.

Thus, according to the Sakharov conditions, which are generally accepted, CP violation is much more than a peculiar detail of the standard model of particle theory. It is essential to create the universe as we observe it. It has been accurately described as "why we exist". As already mentioned, the CP violation observed starting in 1964 in kaon decays and later around 2000 in B-meson decay is not enough to produce enough matter–antimatter asymmetry. This is certainly to be listed as one of the most important open questions.

Another open question is the appearance of three quark–lepton families. One attractive idea is that it is due to anomaly cancellation and can be seen in a generalisation of the standard model in which the electroweak gauge group $SU(2)_L \times U(1)_Y$ is extended to $SU(3)_L \times U(1)_X$. A weird model suggested by the first author predicts the existence of doubly charged gauge bosons $Y^{\pm\pm}$ with spin one, mass close to 1400 GeV, and decays into pairs of like-sign leptons such as $Y^{--} \to \mu^- \mu^-$ and so on.

One feature of scientific progress is that answering one question usually generates one or more new questions. In this book, we have discussed the Darwinian evolution of particle theory ideas from the ancient Greeks in Chapter 1 through the Renaissance up until the present time. The progress in particle theory in the last 70 years and of theoretical cosmology in the last 20 has been truly astonishing and the rate of acquiring new knowledge is constantly increasing.

In this chapter, we have discussed many open questions in both of these directions, the very small and the very large. The two have growing interplay because they are linked by the early universe when both were directly relevant.

We hope to have convinced our reader that the present is a particularly exciting time. As always, it is experimental and observational data which are the main driving force as only they can provide a reliable basis on which to build theory which then can make testable predictions.

In our final chapter, as a complete change, we look at the writing of William Shakespeare (1564–1616) and muse, as Lucretius would, about how it might be interpreted with respect to particle theory. He can readily be bracketed with Newton and Darwin as a third English genius, just one who is not normally associated with science.

## Chapter 10

# Shakespeare

Here, we list some musings of Darwin and Shakespeare. After a few of Darwin's evolutionary ideas, we quote Shakespeare.

Whether there are environmental changes or not, evolution can occur from various reasons. With environmental changes, of course evolution will favour variations that result in a better fitness in the new environment. Even without environmental changes, the status quo will be difficult to be maintained in a real world.

Theories favoured by eminent physicists:

> "Natural selection favors both extremes of continuous variation. Over time, the two extreme variations will become more common and the intermediate states will be less common or lost."
>
> (Disruptive selection)

Teaching excellent students:

> "Sexual selection is a type of selection in which the forces determined by mate choice act to cause one genotype to mate more frequently than another genotype."
>
> (Sexual selection)

Engineering a theory looking different from others:

> "Males look different from females of the species. Some of the most obvious examples involve animals that attract mates by virtue of their appearance, such as peacocks with larger, more flamboyant tail fans. The male that is most attractive will win the right to mate with the female."
>
> (Sexual diomorphism)

The band wagon effect among particle theorists:

"Over time the favored extreme will become more common and the other extreme will be less common or lost."

(Directional selection)

Same transparencies among particle physicists' talks:

"Natural selection favors the intermediate states of continuous variation. Over time, the intermediate states become more common and each extreme variation will become less common or lost."

(Stabilising selection)

Nominating the same group member to various prizes:

"Natural selection favors a trait that benefits related members of a group. Altruistic behaviors of the worker bees are a result of kin selection, and are best illustrated by animals with complex social behaviors."

(Kin selection)

Choosing excellent speakers at big conferences:

"As with appearance, males that have the most attractive mating ritual potentially win the right to mate with the female."

(Mating)

Big Bang versus stationary state of the universe:

"In species with males that battle over rights to mate with females, such as elephants and deer, the male that wins a fight because he is the strongest, most dominant, or most intelligent will win the right to mate with the female. Over time, the features that allow the males to win (larger tusks, larger antlers, larger body size) will become more common."

(Dual fight)

Given his general acceptance as the greatest writer of the English language, it is not surprising that Shakespeare's plays and sonnets are so frequently quoted. Here, we apply the selected lines he wrote to the fascinating subject of particle theory.

Lack of a complete particle theory:

> "There are more things in heaven and earth, Horatio, than are dreamt of in your philosophy."
>
> (Hamlet)

Darwin and Newton were both born in England, which has one percent of the total population:

> "This royal throne of kings, this sceptred isle, this blessed plot, this earth, this realm, this England."
>
> (Richard II)

In favour of collaboration between particle theorists:

> "Let me not to the marriage of true minds admit impediments."
>
> (Sonnet)

The difficult challenge of particle theory:

> "Lord, what fools these mortals be!"
>
> (A Midsummer Night's Dream)

About naming particles:

> "What's in a name? A rose by any name would smell as sweet."
>
> (Romeo and Juliet)

On the future of particle theory:

> "We know what we are, but know not what we may be."
>
> (Hamlet)

The quality of a particle theory paper:

> "There is nothing either good or bad, but thinking makes it so."
>
> (Hamlet)

So many parameters in the Standard Model:

> "Now is the winter of our discontent."
>
> (Richard III)

Quantum gravity:

"To be, or not to be: that is the question."

(Hamlet)

Atomism:

"It is as easy to count atomies as to resolve the propositions of a lover."

(As You Like It)

Understanding Nature:

"In nature's infinite book of secrecy, a little I can read."

(Antony and Cleopatra)

Aristotle:

"SIR TOBY BELCH: Does not our lives consist
of the four elements?
SIR ANDREW AGUECHEEK:
Faith, so they say; but I think it rather consists
of eating and drinking.
SIR TOBY BELCH:
Thou'rt a scholar; let us therefore eat and drink."

(Twelfth Night)

Unimportance of fame:

"I would give all my fame for a pot of ale, and safety."

(Henry V)

Becoming an established particle theorist:

"Men at some time are masters of their fates.
The fault, dear Brutus, is not in our stars,
But in ourselves, that we are underlings."

(Julius Caesar)

Achieving greatness:

"Some are born great, some achieve greatness, and
some have greatness thrust upon them."

(Twelfth Night)

Time:

"Come what come may, time and the hour runs
through the roughest day."

(Macbeth)

Self-unimportance:

"We are such stuff as dreams are made on;
and our little life is rounded with a sleep."

(The Tempest)

Playwright's view of particle theorists:

"All the world's a stage and all the men and
women merely players."

(As you like it)

A particle theory's superficial attractiveness:

"All that glisters is not gold."

(Merchant of Venice)

Persistence of time:

"When I do count the clock that tells the time,
And see the brave day sunk in hideous night;
When I behold the violet past prime,
And sable curls all silver'd o'er with white;
When lofty trees I see barren of leaves
Which erst from heat did canopy the herd,
And summer's green all girded up in sheaves
Borne on the bier with white and bristly beard,
Then of thy beauty do I question make,
That thou among the wastes of time must go,
Since sweets and beauties do themselves forsake
And die as fast as they see others grow;
And nothing 'gainst Time's scythe can make defence
Save breed, to brave him when he takes thee hence."

(Sonnet)

Waiting for the result of particle experiment:

"I am to wait, though waiting so be hell."

(Sonnet)

Asymptotic freedom:

"How heavy do I journey on the way,
When what I seek, my weary travel's end,
Doth teach that ease and that repose to say, Thus far the miles are measured from thy friend!
The beast that bears me, tired with my woe,
Plods dully on, to bear that weight in me,
As if by some instinct the wretch did know
His rider lov'd not speed, being made from thee:
The bloody spur cannot provoke him on,
That sometimes anger thrusts into his hide,
Which heavily he answers with a groan,
More sharp to me than spurring to his side;
For that same groan doth put this in my mind,
My grief lies onward, and my joy behind."

(Sonnet)

Effect of tiredness:

"Is this a dagger which I see before me,
The handle toward my hand? Come, let me clutch thee!
I have thee not, and yet I see thee still.
Art thou not, fatal vision, sensible
To feeling as to sight? or art thou but
A dagger of the mind, a false creation
Proceeding from the heat-oppressed brain?"

(Macbeth)

Music inspires particle theorists:

"If music be the food of love, play on.
Give me excess of it that, surfeiting,
The appetite may sicken, and so die."

(Twelfth Night)

When a theoretical result is suspicious:

"Something is rotten in the state of Denmark."

(Hamlet)

Quantum gravity, longer version:

"To be, or not to be, that is the question,
Whether 'tis nobler in the mind to suffer
The slings and arrows of outrageous fortune,
Or to take arms against a sea of troubles,
And by opposing end them? To die: to sleep;
No more; and by a sleep to say we end
The heart-ache and the thousand natural shocks
That flesh is heir to, 'tis a consummation
Devoutly to be wish'd. To die, to sleep;
To sleep: perchance to dream: ay, there's the rub;
For in that sleep of death what dreams may come
When we have shuffled off this mortal coil,
Must give us pause: there's the respect
That makes calamity of so long life;
For who would bear the whips and scorns of time,
The oppressor's wrong, the proud man's contumely,
The pangs of despised love, the law's delay,
The insolence of office and the spurns
That patient merit of the unworthy takes,
When he himself might his quietus make
With a bare bodkin? who would fardels bear,
To grunt and sweat under a weary life,
But that the dread of something after death,
The undiscover'd country from whose bourn
No traveller returns, puzzles the will
And makes us rather bear those ills we have
Than fly to others that we know not of?
Thus conscience does make cowards of us all;
And thus the native hue of resolution
Is sicklied o'er with the pale cast of thought,
And enterprises of great pith and moment
With this regard their currents turn awry,
And lose the name of action. — Soft you now!
The fair Ophelia! Nymph, in thy orisons
Be all my sins remember'd."

(Hamlet)

Becoming established, longer version:

"Why, man, he doth bestride the narrow world
Like a Colossus, and we petty men
Walk under his huge legs and peep about
To find ourselves dishonourable graves.
Men at some time are masters of their fates:
The fault, dear Brutus, is not in our stars,
But in ourselves, that we are underlings.
Brutus and Caesar: what should be in that 'Caesar'?
Why should that name be sounded more than yours?
Write them together, yours is as fair a name;
Sound them, it doth become the mouth as well;
Weigh them, it is as heavy; conjure with 'em,
Brutus will start a spirit as soon as Caesar.
Now, in the names of all the gods at once,
Upon what meat doth this our Caesar feed,
That he is grown so great? Age, thou art shamed!
Rome, thou hast lost the breed of noble bloods!
When went there by an age, since the great flood,
But it was famed with more than with one man?
When could they say till now, that talk'd of Rome,
That her wide walls encompass'd but one man?
Now is it Rome indeed and room enough,
When there is in it but one only man.
O, you and I have heard our fathers say,
There was a Brutus once that would have brook'd
The eternal devil to keep his state in Rome
As easily as a king."

(Julius Caesar)

About great scientists being born in England:

"Once more unto the breach, dear friends, once more;
Or close the wall up with our English dead.
In peace there's nothing so becomes a man
As modest stillness and humility:
But when the blast of war blows in our ears,
Then imitate the action of the tiger;
Stiffen the sinews, summon up the blood,
Disguise fair nature with hard-favour'd rage;
Then lend the eye a terrible aspect;

Let pry through the portage of the head
Like the brass cannon; let the brow o'erwhelm it
As fearfully as doth a galled rock
O'erhang and jutty his confounded base,
Swill'd with the wild and wasteful ocean.
Now set the teeth and stretch the nostril wide,
Hold hard the breath and bend up every spirit
To his full height. On, on, you noblest English.
Whose blood is fet from fathers of war-proof!
Fathers that, like so many Alexanders,
Have in these parts from morn till even fought
And sheathed their swords for lack of argument:
Dishonour not your mothers; now attest
That those whom you call'd fathers did beget you.
Be copy now to men of grosser blood,
And teach them how to war. And you, good yeoman,
Whose limbs were made in England, show us here
The mettle of your pasture; let us swear
That you are worth your breeding; which I doubt not;
For there is none of you so mean and base,
That hath not noble lustre in your eyes.
I see you stand like greyhounds in the slips,
Straining upon the start. The game's afoot:
Follow your spirit, and upon this charge
Cry 'God for Harry, England, and Saint George!'."

(Henry V)

Requesting divine intervention:

"Slave, I have set my life upon a cast,
And I will stand the hazard of the die:
I think there be six Richmonds in the field;
Five have I slain to-day instead of him.
A horse! a horse! my kingdom for a horse!"

(Richard III)

Particle theories are often publicly debated like the oratory against (Brutus) and for (Antony) Julius Caesar at the funeral.

Brutus:

"Be patient till the last.
Romans, countrymen, and lovers! hear me for my

cause, and be silent, that you may hear: believe me
for mine honour, and have respect to mine honour, that
you may believe: censure me in your wisdom, and
awake your senses, that you may the better judge.
If there be any in this assembly, any dear friend of
Caesar's, to him I say, that Brutus' love to Caesar
was no less than his. If then that friend demand
why Brutus rose against Caesar, this is my answer: —
Not that I loved Caesar less, but that I loved
Rome more. Had you rather Caesar were living and
die all slaves, than that Caesar were dead, to live
all free men? As Caesar loved me, I weep for him;
as he was fortunate, I rejoice at it; as he was
valiant, I honour him: but, as he was ambitious, I
slew him. There is tears for his love; joy for his
fortune; honour for his valour; and death for his
ambition. Who is here so base that would be a
bondman? If any, speak; for him have I offended.
Who is here so rude that would not be a Roman? If
any, speak; for him have I offended. Who is here so
vile that will not love his country? If any, speak;
for him have I offended. I pause for a reply.
Then none have I offended. I have done no more to
Caesar than you shall do to Brutus. The question of
his death is enrolled in the Capitol; his glory not
extenuated, wherein he was worthy, nor his offences
enforced, for which he suffered death.
Here comes his body, mourned by Mark Antony: who,
though he had no hand in his death, shall receive
the benefit of his dying, a place in the
commonwealth; as which of you shall not? With this
I depart, — that, as I slew my best lover for the
good of Rome, I have the same dagger for myself,
when it shall please my country to need my death."

(Julius Caesar)

And, the response:

Antony:

"Friends, Romans, countrymen, lend me your ears;
I come to bury Caesar, not to praise him.

The evil that men do lives after them;
The good is oft interred with their bones;
So let it be with Caesar. The noble Brutus
Hath told you Caesar was ambitious:
If it were so, it was a grievous fault,
And grievously hath Caesar answer'd it.
Here, under leave of Brutus and the rest —
For Brutus is an honourable man;
So are they all, all honourable men —
Come I to speak in Caesar's funeral.
He was my friend, faithful and just to me:
But Brutus says he was ambitious;
And Brutus is an honourable man.
He hath brought many captives home to Rome
Whose ransoms did the general coffers fill:
Did this in Caesar seem ambitious?
When that the poor have cried, Caesar hath wept:
Ambition should be made of sterner stuff:
Yet Brutus says he was ambitious;
And Brutus is an honourable man.
You all did see that on the Lupercal
I thrice presented him a kingly crown,
Which he did thrice refuse: was this ambition?
Yet Brutus says he was ambitious;
And, sure, he is an honourable man.
I speak not to disprove what Brutus spoke,
But here I am to speak what I do know.
You all did love him once, not without cause:
What cause withholds you then, to mourn for him?
O judgment! thou art fled to brutish beasts,
And men have lost their reason. Bear with me
My heart is in the coffin there with Caesar,
And I must pause till it come back to me."

(Julius Caesar).

England as the birthplace of Newton and Darwin:

"Methinks I am a prophet new inspired
And thus expiring do foretell of him:
His rash fierce blaze of riot cannot last,
For violent fires soon burn out themselves;
Small showers last long, but sudden storms are short;

He tires betimes that spurs too fast betimes;
With eager feeding food doth choke the feeder:
Light vanity, insatiate cormorant,
Consuming means, soon preys upon itself.
This royal throne of kings, this scepter'd isle,
This earth of majesty, this seat of Mars,
This other Eden, demi-paradise,
This fortress built by Nature for herself
Against infection and the hand of war,
This happy breed of men, this little world,
This precious stone set in the silver sea,
Which serves it in the office of a wall,
Or as a moat defensive to a house,
Against the envy of less happier lands,
This blessed plot, this earth, this realm, this England,
This nurse, this teeming womb of royal kings,
Fear'd by their breed and famous by their birth,
Renowned for their deeds as far from home,
For Christian service and true chivalry,
As is the sepulchre in stubborn Jewry,
Of the world's ransom, blessed Mary's Son,
This land of such dear souls, this dear dear land,
Dear for her reputation through the world,
Is now leased out, I die pronouncing it,
Like to a tenement or pelting farm:
England, bound in with the triumphant sea
Whose rocky shore beats back the envious siege
Of watery Neptune, is now bound in with shame,
With inky blots and rotten parchment bonds:
That England, that was wont to conquer others,
Hath made a shameful conquest of itself.
Ah, would the scandal vanish with my life,
How happy then were my ensuing death!"

(Richard II)

Dark matter:

"O, then the earth shook to see the heavens on fire,
And not in fear of your nativity.
Diseased nature oftentimes breaks forth
In strange eruptions; oft the teeming earth

Is with a kind of colic pinch'd and vex'd
By the imprisoning of unruly wind
Within her womb; which, for enlargement striving,
Shakes the old beldam earth and topples down
Steeples and moss-grown towers. At your birth
Our grandam earth, having this distemperature,
In passion shook."

(Henry IV)

Eclipses of the Sun and Moon:

"These late eclipses in the sun and moon portend
no good to us: though the wisdom of nature can
reason it thus and thus, yet nature finds itself
scourged by the sequent effects: love cools,
friendship falls off, brothers divide: in
cities, mutinies; in countries, discord; in
palaces, treason; and the bond cracked 'twixt son
and father. This villain of mine comes under the
prediction; there's son against father: the king
falls from bias of nature; there's father against
child. We have seen the best of our time:
machinations, hollowness, treachery, and all
ruinous disorders, follow us disquietly to our
graves. Find out this villain, Edmund; it shall
lose thee nothing; do it carefully. And the
noble and true-hearted Kent banished! his
offence, honesty! 'Tis strange."

(King Lear)

Imperfections in a particle theory:

"Roses have thorns, and silver fountains mud:
Clouds and eclipses stain both moon and sun,
And loathsome canker lives in sweetest bud."

(Sonnet)

Permanent contribution to particle theory:

"Not marble, nor the gilded monuments
Of princes, shall outlive this powerful rhyme."

(Sonnet)

Big bang or cyclic bounce:

"The hour's now come;
The very minute bids thee ope thine ear;
Obey and be attentive. Canst thou remember
A time before we came unto this cell?
I do not think thou canst, for then thou wast not
Out three years old."

(The Tempest)

Fate of the universe:

"These our actors,
As I foretold you, were all spirits, and
Are melted into air, into thin air,
And, like the baseless fabric of vision,
The cloud-capped towers, the gorgeous palaces,
The solemn temples, the great globe itself,
Yea, all which it inherit, shall dissolve
And, like this insubstantial pageant faded,
Leave not a rack behind. We are such stuff
As dreams are made on, and our little life
Is rounded with sleep."

(The Tempest)

Abandoning a failed particle theory:

"I will have none on't. We shall lose our time
And all be turned to barnacles, or to apes
With foreheads villainous low."

(The Tempest)

Dark energy:

"This thing of darkness
I Acknowledge mine."

(The Tempest)

Creativity:

"Thought is free."

(The Tempest)

Eschewing materialism:

"Me, poor man, my library
Was dukedom large enough."

(The Tempest)

Knowledge:

"They say miracles are past;
and we have our philosophical persons,
to make modern and familiar, things supernatural and causeless.
Hence is it that we make trifles of terrors,
ensconcing ourselves into seeming knowledge,
when we should submit ourselves to an unknown fear."

(All's Well That Ends Well)

The standard model:

"Age cannot wither her,
nor custom stale her infinite variety."

(Antony and Cleopatra)

Lunar eclipse:

"Alack, our terrene moon
Is now eclipsed; and it portends alone
The fall of Antony!"

(Antony and Cleopatra)

Playwright's view of particle theorists, longer version:

"All the world's a stage,
And all the men and women merely players;
They have their exits and their entrances,
And one man in his time plays many parts,
His acts being seven ages. At first, the infant,
Mewling and puking in the nurse's arms.
Then the whining schoolboy, with his satchel
And shining morning face, creeping like snail
Unwillingly to school. And then the lover,
Sighing like furnace, with a woeful ballad
Made to his mistress' eyebrow. Then a soldier,

Full of strange oaths and bearded like the pard,
Jealous in honor, sudden and quick in quarrel,
Seeking the bubble reputation
Even in the cannon's mouth. And then the justice,
In fair round belly with good capon lined,
With eyes severe and beard of formal cut,
Full of wise saws and modern instances;
And so he plays his part. The sixth age shifts
Into the lean and slippered pantaloon,
With spectacles on nose and pouch on side;
His youthful hose, well saved, a world too wide
For his shrunk shank, and his big manly voice,
Turning again toward childish treble, pipes
And whistles in his sound. Last scene of all,
That ends this strange eventful history,
Is second childishness and mere oblivion,
Sans teeth, sans eyes, sans taste, sans everything."

(As You Like It)

Speed of light:

"Time travels at different speeds for different people.
I can tell you who time strolls for, who it trots for,
who it gallops for, and who it stops cold for."

(As You Like It)

Teaching:

"It is far easier for me to teach twenty what were right to be done, than be one of the twenty to follow mine own teaching."

(As You Like It)

Action:

"Action is eloquence."

(Coriolanus)

Elegant theory:

"O, why should nature build so foul a den,
Unless the gods delight in tragedies?"

(Titus Andronicus)

Time:

"Time hath, my lord, a wallet at his back,
Wherein he puts alms for Oblivion,
A great-siz'd monster of ingratitudes.
Those scraps are good deeds past, which are devour'd
As fast as they are made, forgot as soon
As done"

(Troilus and Cressida)

Greatness:

"Be not afraid of greatness."

(Twelfth Night)

Comets:

"When beggars die there are no comets seen;
The heavens themselves blaze forth the death of princes."

(Julius Caesar)

Life and death:

"Ay, but to die, and go we know not where;
To lie in cold obstruction, and to rot;
This sensible warm motion to become
A kneaded clod; and the delighted spirit
To bathe in fiery floods, or to reside
In thrilling region of thick-ribbed ice;
To be imprison'd in the viewless winds,
And blown with restless violence round about
The pendant world; or to be worst than worst
Of those lawless and incertain thought
Imagine howling? 'tis too horrible!
The weariest and most loathed worldly life
That age, ache, penury, and imprisionment
Can lay on nature is a paradise
To what we fear of death."

(Measure for Measure)

Coloured quarks:

"LEPIDUS: What colour is it of?
ANTONY: Of its own colour, too."

(Antony and Cleopatra)

Physic(s)

"Throw physic to the dogs; I'll none of it."

(Macbeth)

Philosophy of physics:

"For there was never yet philosopher
That could endure the toothache patiently,
However they have writ the style of gods,
And made a push at chance and sufferance."

(Much Ado About Nothing)

Music and mathematics:

"I do present you with a man of mine
Cunning in music and the mathematics
To instruct her fully in those sciences."

(Taming of the Shrew)

Philosophy about particle theory:

"It goes so heavily with my disposition that this goodly frame,
the earth, seems to me a sterile promontory.
This most excellent canopy the air, look you,
this brave o'erhanging, this majestic roof
fretted with golden fire —
why, it appears no other thing to me
than a foul and pestilent congregation of vapours.
What a piece of work is a man.
How noble in reason, how infinite in faculty,
in form and moving,
how express and admirable, in action, how like an angel!
in apprehension, how like a god —
the beauty of the world,
the paragon of animals! And yet to me,
what is this quintessence of dust?

Man delights not me?
no, nor woman neither,
though by your smiling you seem to say so."

(Hamlet)

Choice of research project:

"Music and poesy use to quicken you;
The mathematics and the metaphysics?
Fall to them as you find your stomach serves you.
No profit grows where is no pleasure ta?en:
In brief, sir, study what you most affect."

(Taming of the Shrew)

Impossibility to predict the future:

"Not from the stars do I my judgement pluck,
And yet methinks I have astronomy.
But not to tell of good or evil luck,
Of plagues, of dearths, or season's quality;
Nor can I fortune to brief minutes tell,
Pointing to each his thunder, rain, and wind,
Or say with princes if it shall go well?"

(Sonnet)

Astronomical query:

"And teach me how
To name the bigger light, and how the less,
That burn by day and night?"

(The Tempest)

Properties of time:

"Love is begun by time,
And time qualifies the spark and fire of it"

(Hamlet)

Infinity:

"My bounty is as boundless as the sea,
My love as deep; the more I give to thee,
The more I have, for both are infinite"

(Romeo and Juliet)

Stars and Sun:

"Doubt thou the stars are fire;
Doubt that the sun doth move;
Doubt truth to be a liar;
But never doubt I love."

(Hamlet)

Blaming the Sun, Moon and Stars:

"We make guilty of our disasters the sun,
the moon, and the stars;
as if we were villians by compulsion."

(King Lear)

Higher authority:

"You here shall swear upon this sword of justice,
That you, Cleomenes and Dion, have
Been both at Delphos, and from thence have brought
The seal'd-up oracle, by the hand deliver'd
Of great Apollo's priest; and that, since then,
You have not dared to break the holy seal
Nor read the secrets in't."

(Winter's Tale)

Introspection in solitude:

"Now I am alone.
O, what a rogue and peasant slave am I!
Is it not monstrous that this player here,
But in a fiction, in a dream of passion,
Could force his soul so to his own conceit
That from her working all his visage wann'd,
Tears in his eyes, distraction in's aspect,
A broken voice, and his whole function suiting
With forms to his conceit? and all for nothing!
For Hecuba! What's Hecuba to him, or he to Hecuba,
That he should weep for her? What would he do,
Had he the motive and the cue for passion
That I have? He would drown the stage with tears
And cleave the general ear with horrid speech,
Make mad the guilty and appal the free,

Confound the ignorant, and amaze indeed
The very faculties of eyes and ears. Yet I,
A dull and muddy-mettled rascal, peak,
Like John-a-dreams, unpregnant of my cause,
And can say nothing; no, not for a king,
Upon whose property and most dear life
A damn'd defeat was made. Am I a coward?
Who calls me villain? breaks my pate across?
Plucks off my beard, and blows it in my face?
Tweaks me by the nose? gives me the lie i' the throat,
As deep as to the lungs? who does me this? Ha!
'Swounds, I should take it: for it cannot be
But I am pigeon-liver'd and lack gall
To make oppression bitter, or ere this
I should have fatted all the region kites
With this slave's offal: bloody, bawdy villain!
Remorseless, treacherous, lecherous, kindless villain!
O, vengeance! Why, what an ass am I! This is most brave,
That I, the son of a dear father murder'd,
Prompted to my revenge by heaven and hell,
Must, like a whore, unpack my heart with words,
And fall a-cursing, like a very drab,
A scullion!. Fie upon't! foh! About, my brain! I have heard
That guilty creatures sitting at a play
Have by the very cunning of the scene
Been struck so to the soul that presently
They have proclaim'd their malefactions;
For murder, though it have no tongue, will speak
With most miraculous organ. I'll have these players
Play something like the murder of my father
Before mine uncle: I'll observe his looks;
I'll tent him to the quick: if he but blench,
I know my course. The spirit that I have seen
May be the devil: and the devil hath power
To assume a pleasing shape; yea, and perhaps
Out of my weakness and my melancholy,
As he is very potent with such spirits,
Abuses me to damn me: I'll have grounds
More relative than this: the play's the thing
Wherein I'll catch the conscience of the king."

(Hamlet)

Memories of a late colleague:

"Alas, poor Yorick! I knew him, Horatio: a fellow
of infinite jest, of most excellent fancy: he hath
borne me on his back a thousand times; and now, how
abhorred in my imagination it is! my gorge rims at
it. Here hung those lips that I have kissed I know
not how oft. Where be your gibes now? your
gambols? your songs? your flashes of merriment,
that were wont to set the table on a roar? Not one
now, to mock your own grinning? quite chap-fallen?
Now get you to my lady's chamber, and tell her, let
her paint an inch thick, to this favour she must
come; make her laugh at that. Prithee, Horatio, tell
me one thing."

(Hamlet)

Confusion:

"Confusion now hath made his masterpiece."

(Macbeth)

More confusion:

"O, full of scorpions is my mind!"

(Macbeth)

Permanence of the Pole Star:

"I am constant as the northern star,
Of whose true-fixed and resting quality
There is no fellow in the firmament."

(Julius Caesar)

Mystery of comets:

"By being seldom seen, I could not stir
But like a comet I was wondered at."

(Henry IV)

Passage of time:

"And so, from hour to hour, we ripe and ripe.
And then, from hour to hour, we rot and rot;
And thereby hangs a tale."

(As You Like It)

All particle theorists are equivalent:

"I think the King is but a man, as I am.
The violet smells to him as it doth to me.
The element shows to him as it doth to me.
All his senses have but human conditions.
His ceremonies laid by,
in his nakedness he appears but a man."

(Henry V)

Dangerous to think too much:

"Let me have men about me that are fat;
sleek-headed men and such as sleep o?night.
Yon Cassius has a lean and hungry look.
He thinks too much.
Such men are dangerous."

(Julius Caesar)

Crazy ideas may be correct:

"Though this be madness,
yet there is method in't."

(Hamlet)

Lack of diplomacy:

"My lord Sebastian,
The truth you speak doth lack some gentleness,
And time to speak it in — you rub the sore
When you should bring the plaster."

(The Tempest)

Preference for a dream world:

"Sometimes a thousand twangling instruments
Will him about mine ears; and sometime voices,

That if I then had waked after long sleep,
Will make me sleep again, and then in dreaming
The clouds methought would open and show riches
Ready to drop upon me, that when I waked
I cried to dream again."

(The Tempest)

Past may not determine future:

"She that is Queen of Tunis; she that dwells
Ten leagues beyond man's life; she that from Naples
Can have no note, unless the sun were post?
The Man i' th' Moon's too slow? till new-born chins
Be rough and razorable; she that from whom
We all were sea-swallow'd, though some cast again
(And by that destiny) to perform an act
Whereof what's past is prologue; what to come,
In yours and my discharge."

(The Tempest)

Can the Moon influence particle theory:

"Therefore the moon, the governess of floods,
Pale in her anger washes all the air,
That rheumatic diseases do abound;
And through this distemperature we see
The seasons alter: hoary-headed frosts
Fall in the fresh lap of the crimson rose."

(A Midsummer Night's Dream)

Only humans, not animals, do particle theory:

"There's nothing situate under heaven's eye
But hath his bond in earth, in sea, in sky.
The beasts, the fishes, and the winged fowls
Are their males' subjects and at their controls.
Man, more divine, the master of all these,
Lord of the wide world and wild wat'ry seas,
Indu'd with intellectual sense and souls,
Of more pre-eminence than fish and fowls,
Are masters to their females, and their lords;
Then let your will attend on their accords."

(The Comedy of Errors)

Relation of Earth to Outer Space:

"The poet's eye, in a fine frenzy rolling,
doth glance from heaven to Earth, from Earth to heaven;
and as imagination bodies forth the forms of things unknown,
the poet's pen turns them to shape,
and gives to airy nothing a local habitation
and a name; such tricks hath strong imagination."

(A Midsummer Night's Dream)

Anthropic principle:

"And nature must obey necessity"

(Julius Caesar)

Collaboration, longer version:

"Let me not to the marriage of true minds
Admit impediments. Love is not love
Which alters when it alteration finds,
Or bends with the remover to remove.
O no, it is an ever-fixed mark
That looks on tempests and is never shaken;
It is the star to every wand'ring barque,
Whose worth's unknown, although his height be taken.
Love's not Time's fool, though rosy lips and cheeks
Within his bending sickle's compass come;
Love alters not with his brief hours and weeks,
But bears it out even to the edge of doom.
If this be error and upon me proved,
I never writ, nor no man ever loved."

(Sonnet)

A good particle theory lasts:

"Shall I compare thee to a summer's day?
Thou art more lovely and more temperate:
Rough winds do shake the darling buds of May,
And summer's lease hath all too short a date:
Sometimes too hot the eye of heaven shines,
And too often is his gold complexion dimm'd:
And every fair from fair sometimes declines,
By chance or natures changing course untrimm'd;
By thy eternal summer shall not fade,

Nor lose possession of that fair thou owest;
Nor shall Death brag thou wander'st in his shade,
When in eternal lines to time thou growest:
So long as men can breathe or eyes can see,
So long lives this and this gives life to thee."

(Sonnet)

Advantages of education:

"Educated men are so impressive!"

(Romeo and Juliet)

Happiness:

"My Crown is in my heart, not on my head:
Not deck'd with Diamonds, and Indian stones:
Nor to be seen: my Crown is call'd Content,
A Crown it is, that seldom Kings enjoy"

(Henry VI)

A good question:

"I can call spirits from the vasty deep.
Why so can I, or so can any man.
But will they come when you do call for them?"

(Henry IV)

War and Peace:

"Let me have war, say I:
it exceeds peace as far as day does night;
it's spritely, waking, audible, and full of vent.
Peace is a very apoplexy, lethargy;
mulled, deaf, sleepy, insensible;
a getter of more bastard children
than war's a destroyer of men."

(Coriolaus)

The passage of particles through time:

"When I do count the clock that tells the time,
And see the brave day sunk in hideous night;
When I behold the violet past prime,
And sable curls all silver'd o'er with white;

When lofty trees I see barren of leaves
Which erst from heat did canopy the herd,
And summer's green all girded up in sheaves
Borne on the bier with white and bristly beard,
Then of thy beauty do I question make,
That thou among the wastes of time must go,
Since sweets and beauties do themselves forsake
And die as fast as they see others grow;
And nothing 'gainst Time's scythe can make defence
Save breed, to brave him when he takes thee hence."

(Sonnet)

# Index

Lightning Source UK Ltd.
Milton Keynes UK
UKHW020012230820
368654UK00001B/18